engineering measurements

M = arithmetic Mean

M_o = True Value

X = error

Error = True Value – Reading

V = variation

Variation = difference between main value + Reading

n = number of readings

engineering measurements

Brother B. Austin Barry, F.S.C.

Manhattan College, New York

John Wiley & Sons, Inc., New York · London · Sydney

(Frontispiece: Courtesy Perkin-Elmer Corp., Norwalk, Conn.)

preface

The modern engineer deals more than ever with observational data, much of which is made to finer tolerances by new instruments. Frequently repeated measurements are made where formerly one or two repetitions may have sufficed in accordance with traditional or rule-of-thumb procedure. Recent practice may easily involve procuring a mass of data.

By reason of instrumentation capable of keener measurement as well as an increasing need for greater certitude, "statistical measurements" and "statistical accuracy" have become commonplace terms. This will be more familiar language in the future, and understanding the simple logic of statistics in measurement will be necessary for engineers.

This book treats of errors inherent in making measurements, those errors which cannot be eradicated by evaluating them and applying corrections. The magnitude of these errors is established by means of the probability theory, opening the way to a reasoned assurance of their accuracy. Such statistical accuracy is the only kind available once measurements are refined beyond instrument capabilities, yet it is a valid type of accuracy. The certitude it affords is by no means fictitious.

The student in engineering or technology will find the text understandable at an early level. It should prove immediately helpful in science and engineering work whenever he encounters measurement or the result of measurement. The terminology is simple and standard and the illustrative examples are sufficiently numerous to make the principles easily understood. While the material presented is basic, it is merely introductory; more extended discussion and application of least square theory, Poisson's distribution, correlation, etc., can be found in more advanced textbooks and technical bulletins.

Acknowledgment is hereby made of the assistance of Brother C. Leonard for the use of much material on error theory and significant digits from his manual *Geometrical and Physical Optics*; of Messrs. Philip A. Brach, Francis X. McKelvey, and William A. Keane in preparing portions of the text and the Appendices; of some material from the USAF Aeronautical Chart Information Center on two-dimensional probability; of a *New York Times* report on the "new" inch; and of many other encouraging colleagues who helped during its preparation.

BROTHER B. AUSTIN BARRY

Manhattan College
July 1964

contents

1. Introduction to Measurement, 1

    1–1   Engineering Measurements, 1
    1–2   How Measurements are Used, 1
    1–3   Comparison with Standard, 2
    1–4   Standards of Length, 2
    1–5   Confusion of Length, 3
    1–6   The Official Inch of 1960, 4
    1–7   Availability of Standards, 4
    1–8   Direct and Indirect Measurements, 5
            Problems, 6

2. Measurement Errors, 7

    2–1   Readings, 7
    2–2   Repeated Readings, 8
    2–3   Best Value, 8
    2–4   Mistakes, 9
    2–5   Discrepancy, 9
    2–6   Systematic Errors, 9
    2–7   Types of Systematic Errors, 10
    2–8   Counteracting Systematic Errors, 11
    2–9   Detecting Systematic Errors, 11
    2–10 Accidental Errors, 12
    2–11 Discrepancies Indicative of Accidental Errors, 12
    2–12 Use of the Mean, 13
            Problems, 13

3. *Reliability of Measurements, 15*

    3–1   Accuracy versus Precision, 15
    3–2   Results versus Method, 16
    3–3   Behavior and Occurrence of Accidental Errors, 16
    3–4   The Probability Curve, 18
    3–5   Normal Probability Curve, 18
    3–6   Skewed Probability Curve, 19
    3–7   Least Squares Principle, 19
    3–8   Errors and Residuals, 21
    3–9   Equating Residuals with Accidental Errors, 22
    3–10 Precision an Indicator of Accuracy, 22
           Problems, 23

4. *Probability Theory of Errors, 24*

    4–1   Mean Square Error, 24
    4–2   Standard Deviation, 24
    4–3   Standard Error, 25
    4–4   Frequency Distribution Table, 26
    4–5   Use of Standard Errors, 27
    4–6   Plotting the Histogram and the Probability Curve, 28
    4–7   Normal Probability Distribution Curve, 29
    4–8   Short Method for Standard Deviation, 30
           Problems, 31

5. *Measures of Reliability, 33*

    ·5–1   Definitions, 33
    5–2   Mean, 33
    5–3   Median, 33
    5–4   Mode, 33
    5–5   Scatter, 34
    5–6   Range, 34
    5–7   Mean Deviation, 34
    5–8   Standard Deviation, 35
    5–9   The Sigma Error, 35
    5–10 The Two-Sigma Error, 36
    5–11 The Three-Sigma Error, 36
    5–12 Probable Error, 37
    5–13 Summary Table, 39
           Problems, 40

6. *Reliability of Repeated Measurements, 42*

   6–1   Multiple Measurements, 42
   6–2   Number of Repeated Measurements, 42
   6–3   Rejecting Measurements, 43
   6–4   Maximum Possible Error, 44
   6–5   Use of Maximum Error, 44
   6–6   Significance, 45
   6–7   Using the Standard Error to Compare Sets, 45
   6–8   Standard Error of the Differences between Means, 45
   6–9   Limitation of Standard Error, 47
          Problems, 47

7. *Propagation of Errors in Computing, 49*

   7–1   Remarks, 49
   7–2   Addition of Values Containing Errors, 49
   7–3   Subtraction of Values Containing Errors, 50
   7–4   Multiplication of Values Containing Errors, 50
   7–5   Division of Values Containing Errors, 51
   7–6   Multiplication of Values Containing Errors by a Constant, 52
   7–7   Elevation to a Power of a Quantity Containing an Error, 52
   7–8   Root of Quantity Containing an Error, 53
   7–9   Other Operations, 54
          Problems, 55

8. *Errors and Weights, 56*

   8–1   Weight and Reliability, 56
   8–2   The Weighted Mean, 56
   8–3   Assigning Weights, 57
          Use of Judgment, 57
          Use of Indexes, 58
          Concept of Numbers, 59
   8–4   Equal Weights, 59
   8–5   Equal Weights, with Exact Check Value, 60
   8–6   Equal Weights, with Arbitrary Value, 60
   8–7   Equal Weights of Component and Total, 61
   8–8   Weights Proportional to Number of Measurements, 62

8–9 Weights and Errors, 62
8–10 Weights and the Standard Error, 63
8–11 Weights and Adjustments, 63
8–12 Unequal Weights, with Exact Check Value, 65
Problems, 66

9. *Practical Application of the Theory of Errors in Measurement, 70*

9–1 Remarks, 70
9–2 Standard Deviation a Criterion, 70
9–3 Fixing upon a Maximum Desired Error, 71
9–4 Selecting a "Maximum Error," 71
9–5 Procedure for Limiting the Error, 72
9–6 Standardizing the Procedure, 72
9–7 Utilizing a Standard Procedure, 72
9–8 Setting Specifications for a Standard Procedure, 76
Problems, 77

10. *Two-Dimensional Errors, 79*

10–1 General, 79
10–2 Definition, 79
10–3 The Probability Ellipse, 80
10–4 The Probability Circle, 81
10–5 Elliptical (Circular) Error Evaluation, 83
10–6 Application to Position Accuracy, 85
10–7 Use of Control Systems, 87
Problems, 88

Appendices, 89

A. *Significant Figures in Measurement, 90*
B. *Basic Concepts of Probability and the Normal Probability Curve, 93*
C. *Writing a Taping Specification, 102*
D. *Classifications and Standards of Accuracy (U.S. Coast and Geodetic Survey), 107*
E. *The Geoid, 112*
F. *The Probability Distribution Curve, 116*
G. *Computer Solution of Problems, 124*

Index, 135

engineering measurements

one / introduction to measurement

1-1 Engineering Measurements

Basic to all engineering is design, and basic to all design is the making of measurements. In both science and engineering, the collection of information means measurements.´ Once measurements are made, they must be organized, evaluated, and interpreted.

Whenever measurements are made, errors are made—the single exception being when the measurement is a discrete count (e.g., the number of people in a room). Because no measurement is free from error, steps must be taken to evaluate the accuracy and the precision of the measurement. In order to preclude a false sense of accuracy, one must investigate the nature of error, the sources, types, and magnitude of errors made at various stages of the measurement operation, and the interrelationship of errors. Only thus is it possible to predict the order of magnitude of the error in the final result.

1-2 How Measurements Are Used

In this treatise, linear measurements with scale, tape, and rod and angular measurements with protractor, transit, and theodolite are made. Errors (personal, instrumental, and natural) are studied. They are analyzed to determine whether they are cumulative or in some measure compensatory. Accuracy and precision are differentiated and analysis of measurement is made with a view to designing systems and specifications to achieve certain desired results. Rules of thumb and empirical formulae are analyzed to determine their worth to an engineer, and modern-day tolerances are also examined.

The use of measurements is the lot of every engineer, and most engineers spend some of their time planning and/or designing with measured quantities. There are few engineers who do not themselves make measurements. Although it is true that many of these measurements are made by technicians and subprofessionals, their planning and direction is the full responsibility of the engineering professional whose understanding of the basic principles must guide the planning, design, and execution of the project.

MEASUREMENTS AND STANDARDS

1-3 Comparison with Standard

The word *measurement* implies comparison of a quantity with a standard value of some sort. The quantity of length, weight, direction, time, volume, etc., to be assessed is measured directly or indirectly against a standard. Throughout history we have had standards, more or less fixed: the cubit (elbow to fingertip), the foot (just that), the inch (thumb-joint to tip), etc. Later on, efforts to achieve standards of length shifted to marching men: the pace, the stadia (stride of a man), the mile (1,000 strides), etc. It is said that early map-makers had a difficult job because standards varied from place to place, and reported distances when plotted for map construction resulted in some weird configurations. The Romans, too, injected confusion purposely as a defense measure, to keep their many enemies from learning true distances.

A later standard, the meter, was intended to be one ten-millionth of the distance from equator to pole on the earth's surface, although subsequent observations show that it missed this by a little bit. The inch and the yard (both British) were independently developed, and are related to the meter today through official (and legal) conversion factors.

1-4 Standards of Length

The word *inch* is derived from the Latin *uncia*, or twelfth part, and has been used to measure things in the Anglo-Saxon world since before William the Conqueror. In those days an inch was defined as the width of a man's thumb, an inadequate standard at best. The first real effort to put the inch on a precise basis was made in the days of Edward I (1272–1307), when it was defined as equal to three barley corns, dry and round, laid end to end. This standard proved to be fairly accurate and was used for several centuries. It is only in the past 200 years that much real progress has been made in the field of calibration.

In 1866 the United States for the first time linked the inch to an international standard when, by act of Congress, it pronounced the international prototype meter at Paris as equal to 39.37 in. A few years later, as a result of its participation in the Metric Convention of 1875, this country received a platinum-iridium meter which became the official standard for all American measures of length. In the ensuing decades, the calibration was made even more accurate, and by 1940 the National Bureau of Standards was able to define an inch accurate to one-millionth of an inch. But it was not allowed to rest on this notable accomplishment. A few years ago a group of expert metrologists from the machine-tool industry informed the Bureau that the accuracy of existing gauge blocks was no longer sufficient to meet their advanced needs. They urged the development of an inch accurate to one or two ten-millionths of an inch, a project which is being actively pursued by the Bureau with the collaboration of private industry.

1–5   *Confusion of Length*

But, as many experts pointed out, refinement of the American inch properly called for standardization with the British and Canadian inches. Because of the 1866 act of Congress, the American inch was equal to 2.540005 cm. The British inch was equal to 2.539995 cm, and most experts wanted the United States to adopt the British standard. That infinitesimal difference of 0.00001 cm had immensely complicated the manufacture and interchangeability of precision instruments on either side of the Atlantic during World War II.

But the proposal to adopt the British inch ran into opposition. Although it was backed by the Army, Navy, the National Advisory Committee for Aeronautics, and the National Bureau of Standards, the Coast and Geodetic Survey pointed out that the changeover would present it with formidable problems. The Survey established plane coordinate systems for each of 48 states about 30 years ago. Subsequently, similar systems were established for Hawaii and Alaska. These map systems include some 150,000 triangulation and traverse points, each of which would have to be changed by several feet should the British standard be adopted. By mutual consent, the special problems of the Coast and Geodetic Survey were recognized, and it will continue to use the old-style inch. Most other official bodies of the United States government, however, will switch over to the new inch (equal to 2.54 cm exactly), as the National Advisory Committee on Aeronautics has already done for use in altimetry and airspeed computations and in defining the standard atmosphere.

With the inch set officially at 2.54 cm exactly, the problem has shifted to the definition of the standard meter. Experience has shown that even bars of platinum-iridium kept hermetically sealed at constant temperature are not changeless. The process of atomic disintegration changes them slightly, decade by decade.

1-6 The Official Inch of 1960

But the scientists of the world worked busily on an atomic standard for length measurement. In 1960 international agreement was reached on a specific atomic wavelength, the so-called orange line of the element Krypton 86. The inch was defined as 2.54 cm exactly, and the meter as "equal to 1,650,763.73 wavelengths in vacuum of the radiation corresponding to the transition between the energy levels of 2_{p10} and 5_{d5} of the atom Krypton 86." The inch should now be pretty well nailed down, at least for the foreseeable future.

1-7 Availability of Standards

Since time, temperature, voltage, weight, angular, gravity, and frequency standards have been developed, it is aptly remarked that we live today in a standardized world. Prototypes of almost every standard quantity are kept carefully in France (the meter, the kilogram), in England (the British Standard Yard, the British Imperial Pound), etc. An absolute determination of gravity made at Potsdam in 1904 became, by international agreement, the standard to which all other gravity measurements were referred. Time standards, traditionally maintained at celestial observatories on "standard" clocks checked by star sights, have recently been geared to an invariant "atomic clock." Frequency standards (both audio and radio) and many others also exist in various places in various forms, and all are carefully safeguarded.

To be available for wide use, however, standards have to be copied with great care and distributed. From these copies, working standards are then obtained and widely dispersed, as exemplified in a tape certified for length by the National Bureau of Standards in Washington for an individual who desires such assurance. Even so, these "working" standards are not generally used directly for measurements, but are merely used for comparison with working tools or measuring devices.

In our modern world, more measurements are made and are made more accurately than ever before in history. Measurement and a knowledge thereof must be regarded as basic to engineering of whatever kind and thus vital to our whole civilization. New demands have developed rigorous requirements for accuracy, reliability, and sensitivity of measurements. The slower and more tedious measurement methods have been supplanted by swift and frequently complex indirect methods.

1–8   *Direct and Indirect Measurements*

Direct comparison with a primary or a secondary standard is quite common in length measurement. Analytical chemists use the beam balance to measure (actually, to compare) masses, such measuring being called weighing. A watch is a direct measuring device for time.

More frequently, however, measurements are made through indirect comparison with a standard. Thus a spring balance is used to determine weight by permitting a measurement of the length that a steel spring expands under tension; the usual tire gage gives an indication of air pressure in much the same way; and a mercury thermometer measures temperature by converting volumetric thermal expansion of the fluid into (essentially) a lineal dimension for viewing. In fact, a whole array of instruments in the modern airplane display varying measured electrical inputs to indicate fuel quantity, air speed, pressures, temperatures, direction, rates of flow, etc., many of which are only indirectly measurements of the basic quantities.

Ultimately, however, every measurement must result in a reading or "read-out" since someone at some time must receive the knowledge of a particular comparison to a standard. This reading and its attendant difficulties are the subjects of the ensuing chapters.

PROBLEMS

1. If the Coast and Geodetic Survey were to adopt the new value of the inch, assuming the center of its entire nation-wide system of co-ordinates is in Kansas, by how much would a monument in San Francisco appear to be wrong? (Or would it appear to be wrong?)
2. Could a rubber band serve as a spring balance? Why (not)?
3. Is a digital computer a measuring device?
4. How can the distance from New York to Paris be found by direct measurement?
5. How can the distance to the moon be measured?

two / *measurement errors*

2–1 *Readings*

Generally, when readings of a graduated scale are made, there is an estimation made for the final digit, an estimation of the distance between fine scale graduations, such as 6.27 in Fig. 1. This could be the end of a 50-ft steel tape graduated in tenths, with the half-tenths also marked. Likely, though, it is a rod-reading taken for elevation of the point on which the base of the rod is held.

Note that 6.27 would be the estimate of most people, not 6.26 or 6.28, though these almost surely would be estimated by some people in a series of measurements of the same quantity. Obviously, if the extra care were warranted, a scale with very fine graduations (say, to thousandths) might be used and the readings made with a magnifier, probably to ten thousandths of a foot. Such readings, if repeatedly made by the same (or even a different) person, might vary more widely in the last digit (estimated), but it must be remembered that such readings made to ten thousandths instead of to hundredths are more exact than those of Fig. 1 and the apparently wider fluctuation in the last place is not nearly so serious.

FIGURE 1

2-2 *Repeated Readings*

Assume a series of observed readings for the case above, using the fine graduations and a magnifier, thus reading to ten thousandths of feet (or inches), as in the table. If the readings had been made to thousandths only, all would have been listed as 6.276; if to hundredths, as 6.28; if to tenths only, as 6.3 units. When a set of such observations shows no variation or very little, one may suspect that the observations or measurements are rough or coarse.

READINGS
1. 6.2763
2. 6.2757
3. 6.2761
4. 6.2760
5. 6.2761
6. 6.2758
7. 6.2760
8. 6.2764
9. 6.2759
10. 6.2760

6.27603
Mean

In the case shown at the left, the best value obtainable from the set is the *arithmetic mean*, commonly called the *average*. This is shown as the value 6.27603 or perhaps as 6.2760 units.

It is never possible to obtain absolute correct fourth or fifth decimal-place value in the given instance, simply because the method of measuring was not sufficiently refined. Absolutely correct value does exist, but we could not discover it. What we strive to attain by refined measurements and by techniques of successive measuring is what might be termed a *best available value*.

2-3 *Best Value*

Because the average in the example is the "best available value," we utilize it as being fairly reliable for the purpose at hand. While we do not know that it is incorrect, neither do we have any absolute assurance that it is correct.

What is correctness? Since, for the example shown, we cannot discover a true value, we are forced to assume that the mean value (and, in fact, any of the 10 measured values) contains an error. In this context, error means difference between measured value and true (or correct) value.

It follows, therefore, that we can never discover a "true error" for any measurement. We shall return to this important concept subsequently.

In the above set of measurements, there are two types of errors present which influence the result:

Systematic or constant errors (such as temperature, etc.)

Accidental errors (such as made in setting the zero end, etc.)

2-4 *Mistakes*

The concept of mistakes will be omitted entirely from this discussion; mistakes or blunders are not errors and are never called such. This is not to admit that it unnecessary, however, to guard constantly against mistakes by frequent checking, since mistakes are caused by inattention or carelessness on the part of the observer.

2-5 *Discrepancy*

Discrepancy is a term indicating difference between two or more measurements of a quantity. The existence of a discrepancy is frequently a helpful indication of the need for more careful observations. It is not so obvious that more precise measurements are more likely to show discrepancies than cruder ones, but an example will illustrate.

EXAMPLE. A 9 ft × 12 ft rug may be rather casually measured by a housewife, more to determine if it is a 9 ft or 12 ft rug rather than a 10 ft × 14 ft rug; no one may notice that it is 9.1 ft × 11.8 ft unless it is measured more carefully, say, to discover if it can run wall-to-wall in a 9.0 ft × 12.0 ft room. Thus more careful measurement would reveal a discrepancy between actual and nominal size. Similarly, a careful machinist may measure a cylinder bore as 3.006 in., 3.009 in., 3.004 in., 3.006 in., and 3.004 in. on successive measurements to ascertain its roundness; a more casual measurement perhaps would reveal only that the bore is 3.0 in. with no noticeable discrepancy therefrom in many such casual measurements of several diameters. Thus more precise methods tend to magnify discrepancies or, stated differently, cruder methods tend to hide discrepancies.

SYSTEMATIC OR CUMULATIVE ERRORS

2-6 *Systematic Errors*

Systematic errors, previously referred to as cumulative, must now be considered. A systematic error is one which will invariably have the same magnitude and the same sign under the same given conditions. Thus, a tailor's cloth tape that has been stretched about 5% by overuse will consistently measure a 40-in. waistline as just over 38 in., flattering the customer but providing a tight fit. Once the condition is known, however, the remedy (or correction) can be applied by adding 1 in. to a 20 in. measurement, 1½ in. to a 30 in. measurement, 2 in. to 40 in. measurement, etc.

2-7 Types of Systematic Errors

Systematic errors, then, are attributable to known conditions and vary with these conditions. Such errors can be evaluated and applied, with signs reversed, as corrections to measured quantities. They are of three types:

(*a*) *Natural Errors.* These arise from natural phenomena, and they are really the effects of certain influences that operate to prevent the observer's seeing or reading directly the quantity he is seeking. Some instances are the refraction of light rays, thermal expansion of materials, influence of atmospheric pressure or humidity, etc. For example, an instrument that measures distance by timing a radar-frequency radio wave between two points will give an erroneous distance reading if an adjustment (correction) is not made for the effect of barometric pressure and moisture content in the air on the speed of travel of the radio wave.

(*b*) *Instrumental Errors.* These are the effects of imperfections in the construction or adjustment of the instruments used in making the measurements. Instances are the lack of concentricity of transit circles, graduation errors in scales, less than perfect optics in a telescope, inertia lag of a needle, worn bearings, lack of adjustment of the bubble tube, etc. For example, a spirit level, used to determine the relative elevation of two points, may have the bubble tube axis slightly out of parallel with the sighting axis (line of collimation), giving an erroneous result if the two points are not equally distant from the instrument used for sighting.

(*c*) *Personal Errors.* These depend on the physical limitations and also on the habits of the observer. He may have an auditory lag in noting a time signal, a slight tendency to observe to the right (or to the left) in estimating tenths, or poorly coordinated vision, etc. The amount of such error is usually small, though erratic. For example, in lining up a vernier, the observer may have a tendency to see the line at the left as coincident more frequently than the one at the right, or he may have poor ability in noting time at the beginning and end of an interval when using a stop-watch.

2–8 Counteracting Systematic Errors

While systematic errors are generally cumulative in nature, it is sometimes possible to employ precautionary procedures to prevent their accumulating. For example, if the man on the stop-watch lags in perception by 0.50 sec at both start and finish of a race, he still gets the correct timing. In this case, use the same man to snap both start and finish. If the spirit-level operator sets his instrument equally distant from points A and B, he still gets the correct difference of elevation between A and B, since the $+$ error cancels the $-$ error. Mostly, however, a systematic error does accumulate, as when a shrunken yardstick is laid down successively to set out a tennis court, or an automobile odometer registers 1% high for each mile it travels, or (a common instance) when a watch gains or loses a second per hour. In such cases, it is apparent that a correction can be applied if the magnitude and sign of the systematic error is known.

EXAMPLE. A steel rule 10 ft long is used to measure between two calibration points on the floor of an electronics plant. At the time of the measurement the temperature is 52°F, but the tape is true length (10.0000 ft) only at 68°F. The thermal expansion coefficient for the steel of the tape is 0.00000645 ft/ft. If the reported distance is 127.6120 ft, what is the correct distance?

> Correction (C_t) per tape-length
> $= 0.00000645 \times 10.000 \times (68\text{–}52)$
> $= 0.001032$ ft/tape-length
> Total correction (for 12.7612 tape-lengths)
> $= 0.001032 \times 12.7612$
> $= 0.0132$
> Corrected length $= 127.6120 - 0.0132$
> $\qquad\qquad\qquad = 127.5988$ ft   Ans.

The correction is subtracted because the tape is effectively shortened by the lower temperature, thus giving a reported measurement too large. (The opposite reasoning is employed to apply a correction if we are measuring off the distance from A to set a new point B.)

2–9 Detecting Systematic Errors

While measuring, it is important to prevent systematic errors from impairing the accuracy of the final result. The possibility that a particular systematic error exists may be detected by careful analysis of the methods employed and (most effectively) by comparison with independent results that are known to be fairly accurate, especially results attained by a different method. Correction for systematic errors once detected is not difficult. The detection of such systematic errors, however, depends on the observer's alertness and his knowledge of the natural, instrumental, and personal factors which can influence his procedures.

ACCIDENTAL OR RANDOM ERRORS

2–10 *Accidental Errors*

Accidental errors or errors of observation are random in nature, usually small, and have a tendency to compensate one another. Their presence is indicated in a series of measurements by the appearance of discrepancies. Accidental errors may be either plus or minus; in fact, there is an equal probability that the sign is plus as that it is minus. Furthermore, it cannot be determined just what the sign is, since there is no relationship known between the sign and magnitude of the error on the one hand and any conditions of measurement on the other. They are truly random in occurrence and size.

2–11 *Discrepancies Indicative of Accidental Errors*

Only by studying the discrepancies that occur among repeated measurements of the same quantity is it possible to learn anything about the accidental errors inherent in the measurements (except to know that they are bound to exist).

6.8
7.1
6.9
6.7
6.7
6.9
6.8
7.1
7.0
6.9
2.1469
Mean

For discrepancies (and the consequent residuals) will occur according to a fairly regular pattern when we assume that the instrument used is more refined than the ability of the observer to observe, and that the observations are made with commensurate care and precision.

EXAMPLE. Suppose an extensometer is used to determine a distance between two gage marks on a piece of steel. On the main gage is a reading of 2.14, and on the fine dial are the readings at the left (thousandths of an inch). The digit in the column to right of the decimal point is the value that is estimated by the observer (ten thousandths of an inch). Note that the discrepancies from the mean (residuals) vary up to 0.2 divisions, and be aware that these may be attributable to several kinds of accidental errors: setting the points into the gage holes, imperceptible friction, minor variations of temperature, possible vibration, etc.

2–12   *Use of the Mean*

Again, where we assume that all the observations are made with the same care and under the same conditions, there is no reason to prefer any one observation over any other. Hence, all can be said to be of equal weight, and the arithmetic mean (the unweighted mean) is truly regarded as the best obtainable from the observed quantities. The mean is not, of course, the true value, but only the nearest approximation thereto, subject to improvement or change if other observations become available. For the moment it can be adopted as "correct." (This adoption of the arithmetic mean as the best value obtainable from these observed quantities is a sound and fundamental assumption.)

PROBLEMS

1. What can be done to improve the precision of a single measurement of a distance *AB* (about 35 ft long) on a flat surface?
2. What systematic errors must be corrected so that the above distance *AB* will approach the true value if a tape is used?
3. What natural errors affect the line of sight when using an engineer's level to establish elevation?
4. How can a carpenter's level be tested to determine trueness?
5. Steel fabrication is very carefully conducted at all temperatures, summer and winter, indoors and outdoors, by using an accurate measuring device, without fear that the steel members will subsequently fail to fit together. What is the nature of the device?
6. What advantage will accrue when measuring a steel drum's circumference if a steel tape is carefully wrapped around it ten times and the 10× distance read? Evaluate all the errors of this versus a single wrap-around measurement repeated ten times.
7. Devise a method of measuring the speed of sound by hammering in a repeating pattern (slowly changing frequency) while a distant observer synchronizes sight and sound. What must be measured?

8. If five stopwatches synchronize perfectly at the end of a 10-min. interval, are we assured that
    (a) Each runs uniformly?
    (b) Each keeps accurate time?
9. How can systematic errors be (a) detected? (b) eliminated?
10. In Art. 2–11, is the "9" (last digit in the mean) justified?
11. How many square feet are there in:
    (a) an acre?   (c) 1.000 acre?
    (b) 1.00000 acre?   (d) 1.00 acre?
12. Do we know the speed of light as 186,000.000 miles per second? What is the value exactly?

three / reliability of measurements

3-1 *Accuracy versus Precision*

Before proceeding further, we may well examine accuracy and precision, two concepts that are important to the ensuing treatment of errors.

Precision is descriptive of the degree of care and refinement employed in making a measurement. Accuracy is descriptive of the correctness of the result of the measurement. For example, in the groupings of rifle shots on the targets in Fig. 2 group (*a*) and group (*b*) are very precise, whereas group (*a*) and group (*c*) are very accurate. Group (*a*) may be said to be both precise and accurate, group (*b*) may be said to be precise but not accurate, and group (*c*) may be said to be accurate though not precise.

Accuracy, then, is definable as conformity with true value: it does not have the notion of close conformity with the true, necessarily. Note that in (*a*) as well as in (*c*) above we may properly say the

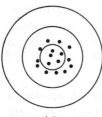
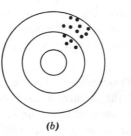
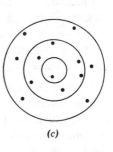

(*a*)   (*b*)   (*c*)

FIGURE 2

person and/or the gun shoots "true," i.e., accurately, although target (c) shows a great deal more scatter.

Precision is definable as closeness of grouping of shots or values, without regard, however, for correctness or truth. On target (b), for instance, the shots are grouped precisely, though not accurately.

EXAMPLE. All the watches in a jewelry store may be reading *precisely* 8:20, though all may be *inaccurate* because standing still. In a school the clocks are controlled by electrical impulses so they run exactly alike to the second. If they are all exactly alike but in error by some minutes, they are precise but not accurate; then if they are all corrected from a radio signal to the right time, they are both precise and accurate.

3–2 *Results versus Method*

If we study each shot of a given group in terms of its variation from the mean, it should become obvious that such a study reveals precision but not accuracy. (Incidentally, it is interesting to consider that the consistent grouping of the shots in a precise pattern in the northeast quadrant of target (b) may be traceable to a systematic error of side wind or poor alignment of gun sight, or a combination thereof.) The discrepancy of each shot from the mean of the group may be called, in statistical terms, the residual or variation of the shot. Analysis of the variations in target (b) will indicate approximately the same precision as in target (a); analysis of target (c) variations will indicate a lower precision for the shooting than in either of the other two groupings, thus a lower precision. (It must be remembered, however, that target (c) shows better accuracy than does target (b). Note that accuracy cannot be determined from residuals or variations.)

Precision, therefore, can be regarded as indicative of the degree of care employed in the operation; accuracy can be regarded as indicative of the exactness of the result. Precision is a result's nearness to another or to the mean value; accuracy is its nearness to the true value.

3–3 *Behavior and Occurrence of Accidental Errors*

The discussion of the behavior and occurrence of accidental errors, which must be assumed to occur at random (or else they are systematic errors, caused by fixed conditions), will here best be illustrated. Suppose a pencil is aimed at an oblong target on the floor and dropped repeatedly from desk height, recording dots on the target as shown in Fig. 3. The pencil is dropped so as to aim at the middle line "O." If dots in each box are counted, the result is as shown in Fig. 4. Then if the numbers are plotted in bar-graph

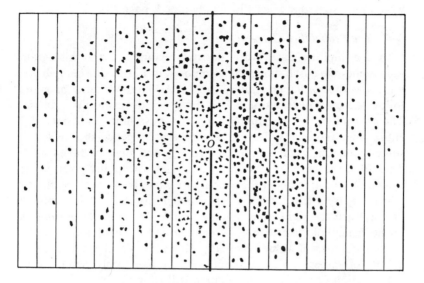

FIGURE 3

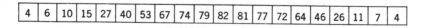

| 4 | 6 | 10 | 15 | 27 | 40 | 53 | 67 | 74 | 79 | 82 | 81 | 77 | 72 | 64 | 46 | 26 | 11 | 7 | 4 |

FIGURE 4

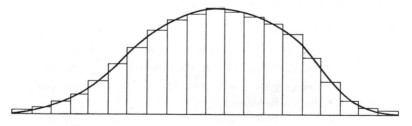

FIGURE 5

form, the result is Fig. 5, which is called a histogram, and on it is superimposed a smooth curve which is discussed next in Art. 3–4. The chance of making a hit in any one target compartment is proportional to the area of the corresponding rectangle. Should the number of pencil-drops be increased to 1,000 or 10,000, the diagram would look something like Fig. 6 (Chapter 4, page 29).

3–4 The Probability Curve

In the limiting case (very narrow rectangles), the histogram approaches the curve shown superimposed in Fig. 5, this curve being known as the *normal probability curve*. All kinds of random errors follow the same distribution law as the pencil-drops in this example. The area under the probability curve is always finite and, since this entire area represents the probability that a pencil-shot will fall somewhere, this area represents certainty and may be taken as 1. Therefore, the probability that an error lies within any given limits is equal to the area under the probability curve between those limits.

It is apparent that the curve (and histogram) of Fig. 5 is leaning a little toward the right, thus lending a little doubt to the normality (or normalcy) of the distribution there plotted. This stems from the limited number of values plotted. However, when given a near-infinity of values, the curve should plot up as entirely symmetrical.

Inspection of the probability curve will show:

(*a*) Small random errors occur more frequently than larger ones, showing that the probability of an error depends on the size of the error.

(*b*) Positive and negative random errors of the same size are about equal in number, making the probability curve symmetrical about the y axis.

(*c*) Very large random errors seldom occur.

3–5 Normal Probability Curve

It can be ascertained from further scrutiny that the normal probability curve is a log function of the form $y = ce^{kx^2}$. In fact, its exact form can be derived as $y = (h/\sqrt{\pi})e^{-h^2x^2}$ though the equation is not frequently handled directly.

We cannot make infinite numbers of measurements every time we need a measured value; a few must suffice. But we then examine the distribution to see if it is similar to the normal distribution curve, or nearly so. Then, when fairly sure it is, we can presume that our observed distribution is part of a whole family of similar measurements in a normal distribution. We can admit the group of measurements to the standard treatment once we can acknowledge that they are a typical distribution. Thus we can use the rules of probability and say of our measurements that the mean is the "best value," that the variance from the mean gives a clue to uncertainty, etc., . . . all the things we can state of an infinite group of measurements.

This is not a cause for misgivings. Instead, the ascribing of qualities of exactness and the assigning of degrees of certainty to our smaller group of measurements, simply by noting the set's resemblance to an "infinitely" large set, is a matter of economics. It is also safe to do. The very resemblance of the small set's distribution of error (shape of the curve) is a matter of confidence attained through similarity.

3–6 *Skewed Probability Curve*

If we have a badly skewed curve, however, we ought to examine our measurements and probably re-make them. There may be a hidden systematic error that has a telling effect on our work. Serious skew would indicate that plus variances are much larger in size than minus variances or vice versa, and the distribution is not normal.

Incidentally, all of the ensuing work is predicated on the normal distribution of results. This will be brought out further in Chapter 9.

3–7 *Least Squares Principle*

If a set of measurements M_1, M_2, M_3, etc., is made, all with equal care and by using the same methods and instruments for each, the precision constant h is the same for all measurements, and the distribution of their random errors (x_1, x_2, x_3, etc.) will be given by the same probability curve. The probabilities of the occurrence of these errors are, then:

$$p_1 = \frac{h}{\sqrt{\pi}} e^{-h^2 x_1^2} \cdot dx_1$$

$$p_2 = \frac{h}{\sqrt{\pi}} e^{-h^2 x_2^2} \cdot dx_2$$

The derivation of this is in Appendix B.

Since the separate measurements are independent events, the probability that the whole set of errors $(x_1, x_2, x_3,$ etc.$)$ will be made is the product of their separate probabilities, or

$$P = p_1 \times p_2 \times p_3, \text{ etc.}$$

$$= \left[\frac{h}{\sqrt{\pi}} \, e^{-h^2(x_1{}^2 + x_2{}^2 + x_3{}^2 + \cdots)} \right] [dx_1, dx_2, dx_3, \ldots]$$

Because in any set of measurements it is more probable that there be a set of small errors than a set of large errors, the set which has the greatest probability will give us the best or most probable value of the quantity measured. Since the precision index h is constant and the differentials dx_1, dx_2, dx_3, etc., are arbitrary quantities, it is evident from the equation above that the probability P is greatest when the exponent of e is the least, i.e., when $x_1{}^2 + x_2{}^2 + x_3{}^2$, etc., is a minimum; in other words, when $\sum x^2$ is a minimum.

Thus the principle of least squares can be expressed as:

The best or most probable value obtainable from a set of measurements of equal precision is that value for which the sum of the squares of the errors is a minimum.

The requirement that the sum of the squares shall be a minimum makes it evident that the arithmetic mean is the best value obtainable from any set of direct measurements that are equally trustworthy.

This means simply that if the arithmetic mean ("average") of a set of several measurements is used as a value to represent the set, it is a better value than any other value because the sum of the squares of the difference of each value from the mean will be the least possible.

EXAMPLE.   Given a set of mileage distances between two points as read from the speedometers (odometers, really) of ten cars, calculate the $\sum v^2$ if $v = M_i - \overline{M}$; then, letting $\overline{M}'$ be any value except the average or mean, again calculate $\sum v^2$ and compare.

Similarly, if any value lower than 104.9 is used (e.g., 104.8), the sum of the squares of the variations therefrom will be greater than 6.30 (actually 6.40 in this case).

	M_i	v	v^2	$v'*$	v'^2
1.	104.8	-0.1	0.01	-0.2	0.04
2.	106.2	$+1.3$	1.69	$+1.2$	1.44
3.	103.7	-1.2	1.44	-1.3	1.69
4.	104.5	-0.4	0.16	-0.5	0.25
5.	104.2	-0.7	0.49	-0.8	0.64
6.	104.9	0.0	0.00	-0.1	0.01
7.	104.1	-0.8	0.64	-0.9	0.81
8.	105.2	$+0.3$	0.09	$+0.2$	0.04
9.	106.2	$+1.3$	1.69	$+1.2$	1.44
10.	105.2	$+0.3$	0.09	$+0.2$	0.04
$\overline{M} =$	104.9		6.30		6.40

* Let $\overline{M}'$ arbitrarily $= 105.0$ and $v' = M_t - \overline{M}'$.

3–8 Errors and Residuals

It is important at this point to distinguish between two concepts that are used interchangeably, viz., error and residual. The absolute magnitude of a quantity can never be determined by measurement, because of the presence of accidental (random) errors. Obviously, then, the error of a measurement can never be determined, since an error is defined as the difference between the measured value and the true value. In practice we use the best value of a series of measurements, viz., the arithmetic mean, in place of the (unknown) true value. The difference between the arithmetic mean and any particular measurement is called the residual for the measurement. The arithmetic mean is used, therefore, as a representation of the true value. The arithmetic mean is truly representative of the series of measurements (and, therefore, equal to the true value) when the distribution of random errors is completely uniform. However, this occurs only when the number of measurements is infinite. Obviously, this is an impossible limitation: we always necessarily work with fewer than this infinite number of measurements. Hereafter, the error will be denoted by x and the residual (variation) by v. It is, of course, evident that since we cannot know the true size of the (accidental) errors (x), we shall most frequently be using residuals or variations from the mean (v) in our formulations.

The following discussion will show the justification for using residuals and variations from the mean.

3–9 Equating Residuals with Accidental Errors

If for a finite number of measurements we assume that

$$\underset{\substack{\text{(Arith.} \\ \text{mean)}}}{M} = \underset{\substack{\text{(True} \\ \text{value)}}}{M_0} - \frac{\sum x}{n}$$

It can be seen that since the errors (x) are as likely to be $+$ as $-$, the quantity $\sum x$ is not large and $\sum x/n$ is still smaller. Hence, the larger the number of measurements, the closer M approaches the true value (M_0) of the quantity measured.

The pattern of occurrence of (accidental) errors is assumed to follow that of the residuals from the mean. Thus, if we assume that

$$\underset{\substack{\text{(Any} \\ \text{residual)}}}{v_1} = \underset{\substack{\text{(Corresponding} \\ \text{error)}}}{x_1} - \frac{\sum x}{n}$$

it is apparent that when the number of measurements is large, residuals are practically equal to the errors. Hence, although we can never determine the true magnitude of a measured quantity, we can determine it as closely as we please by taking enough measurements. In practice, therefore, there is always some uncertainty in the determination of the true magnitude of a quantity. This uncertainty is an estimate of the precision of the measurement, and the precision in turn is an estimate of the accuracy of the measurement (since we have eliminated systematic errors from consideration by applying corrections for them).

3–10 Precision an Indicator of Accuracy

Because the arithmetic mean and its associated residuals give a poor indication of true value when the number of measurements is small, we postulate that the precision of any large set of measurements is an estimate of their accuracy. However, we have seen that as the number of measurements is increased, the value of the residuals approaches that of the errors. Therefore, if a sufficiently large number of measurements is employed, the residuals may be replaced by the errors and vice versa. Thus it is seen that if we narrow the value of the arithmetic mean to a very small range by using residuals, we must conclude that we are also narrowing it down to a very small range with respect to errors, thus approaching very closely to a true (accurate) value.

PROBLEMS

1. Which is more valuable to a baseball team, a pitcher with good precision or one with good accuracy?
2. Draw a histogram of the action of 10 coins shaken and dropped 100 times, along this abscissa:

Tails	10	9	8	7	6	5	4	3	2	1	0
Heads	0	1	2	3	4	5	6	7	8	9	10

3. Can we say that any one of the following sets of numbers is a normal distribution? Why (not)?
   (a) All the numbers from 1 through 25.
   (b) 2.38, 2.37, 2.38, 2.36, 2.36, 2.38, 2.37, 2.36, 2.37, 2.36, 2.36, 2.37, 2.37, 2.38, 2.37, 2.38, 2.37, 2.36, 2.37, 2.38, 2.37, 2.38, 2.37, 2.36.
   (c) 143, 140, 144, 141, 144, 142, 141, 142, 140, 145, 143, 143, 142, 143, 142, 143.
4. In one roll of a single die, what is the probability of rolling a seven? A five? A five or a two? A two, or a three, or a four?
5. In five rolls of a single die, what is the probability of rolling a three once? Twice? Five times?
6. What is the probability of rolling a seven with a pair of dice three consecutive times?
7. Plot a histogram of the sum of four dice shaken and dropped 100 (or 200) times, using along the horizontal axis the values from 4 to 24.

four | probability theory of errors

4–1 *Mean Square Error*

The question now arises as to how to estimate the uncertainty (and hence the precision, and therefore the accuracy) of a measurement. We can use as a measure of the precision any one of several devices, but here we shall speak of the mean square error (the square root of the mean of the squares of the errors). The mean square error is defined (see Art. 3–7) as being equal to

$$\sqrt{\frac{x_1{}^2 + x_2{}^2 + x_3{}^2 + \cdots + x^2}{n}} = \sqrt{\frac{\sum x^2}{n}}$$

This is the mean square error of any single observation of the set.

4–2 *Standard Deviation*

Since we cannot know the values of errors x_1, x_2, x_3, etc., we shall use values we can ascertain, the residuals v_1, v_2, v_3, etc. Before we do, however, it will be necessary to insist on a refinement so as to be in accord with statistical authorities.

We have seen previously that

$$\underset{\substack{\text{(Any} \\ \text{residual)}}}{v_1} = \underset{\substack{\text{(Corresponding} \\ \text{error)}}}{x_1} - \frac{\sum x}{n}$$

By working this relationship into the equation of the *probability curve*, although it is beyond the scope of this treatment, it is possible to establish that the *mean square error* (dealing with errors) and what we call the *standard deviation* (dealing with residuals) are not quite equal. Whereas the mean square error of any single measurement in a set is $\sqrt{\sum x^2/n}$, the standard deviation for any single measurement is defined as:

$$\sigma_s = \sqrt{\frac{\sum v^2}{n-1}} = \sqrt{\frac{v_1{}^2 + v_2{}^2 + v_3{}^2 + \cdots, \text{etc.}}{n-1}}$$

Despite the slight difference, the term *mean square error* is frequently used, however, for σ_s instead of the more proper *mean square variation*, or *mean square deviation*, or simply *standard deviation* (of any single measurement in a set). It may also be noted that sometimes the value σ_s is shown as $\sqrt{\sum v^2/n}$ instead of $\sqrt{\sum v^2/(n-1)}$. The difference between the two becomes less important as the value of n increases.

There is no real harm, once the number of measurements becomes 10, 15, or more, in using either of these formulae. This, too, will explain why it is possible to speak of *mean square error* and *standard deviation* as synonymous and equivalent.

4–3   *Standard Error*

We frequently wish to know something about the uncertainty of the arithmetic mean. It may be reasoned that the uncertainty of the arithmetic mean of a series of measurements is much less than that of any single measurement. In fact, it has been determined (though not herein) that the *mean square error* of the arithmetic mean of a set is properly the mean square error of any single value divided by the square root of the number of measurements. We do not speak of this as the "standard deviation" but call it the *standard error* (of the mean). Thus, the *standard error* of the arithmetic mean equals the standard deviation of any single measurement divided by the square root of the number of measurements.

$$\sigma_m = \frac{\sigma_s}{\sqrt{n}} = \sqrt{\frac{\sum v^2}{n(n-1)}} \approx \frac{\sqrt{\sum v^2}}{\sqrt{n(n)}} = \frac{\sqrt{\sum v^2}}{n}$$

We shall denote standard error by σ_m, and standard deviation by σ_s. The σ_s value may be variously called *sigma*, or *mean square error*, or *root mean square error*, or *standard deviation*. It must be remembered as the square root of the mean of the squares of the deviations from the mean (or variations from the mean). The standard error σ_m is sometimes referred to as the *sigma error of the mean*, confusingly enough. Care must be taken to avoid mixing the two. Standard error is discussed further in Chapter 6.

4–4 *Frequency Distribution Table*

Before continuing, it may be wise to look at two examples and study the meanings of various terms in relation thereto.

EXAMPLE 1. The arithmetic mean (or arithmetic average) is usually easily obtainable, but in some cases it is easier to work with a frequency distribution table. The following may suffice to show this.

To find the arithmetic mean of these values 3.3, 4.0, 3.7, 3.5, 3.7, 3.9, 3.7, 3.6, 3.9, 3.8, 3.6, 3.5, 3.9, 3.5, 3.6, 3.7, 3.4, 3.6, 3.8, 3.5, set up a frequency distribution table as shown here.

Value (X)	f	fx
3.3	1	3.3
3.4	1	3.4
3.5	4	14.0
3.6	4	14.4
3.7	4	14.8
3.8	2	7.6
3.9	3	11.7
4.0	1	4.0
Mean = 3.66	20	73.2

Arithmetic mean:

$$\bar{X} = \frac{\sum fX}{n}$$
$$= \frac{73.2}{20}$$
$$= 3.66$$

EXAMPLE 2. A set of 439 observations was made on a distant rod target. The results shown are again tabulated in a manner adapted to easy plotting and to easy computation of the mean.

Value (feet) x	No. of occurrences f	Product (omit 6.500) fx	Residual (or variation) v (thousandths)	fv	fv^2
6.571	1	71	-7	-7	49
6.572	8	576	-6	-48	288
6.573	18	1,314	-5	-90	450
6.574	27	1,998	-4	-108	432
6.575	36	2,700	-3	-108	324
6.576	43	3,268	-2	-86	172
6.577	53	4,081	-1	-53	53
6.578	55	4,290	0	0	0
6.579	53	4,187	$+1$	$+53$	53
6.580	46	3,680	$+2$	$+92$	184
6.581	36	2,916	$+3$	$+108$	324
6.582	26	2,132	$+4$	$+104$	416
6.583	15	1,245	$+5$	$+75$	375
6.584	13	1,092	$+6$	$+78$	468
6.585	7	595	$+7$	$+49$	343
6.586	2	172	$+8$	$+16$	128
6.5782 (mean)	439 n	34,317 Σfx		1,075 $= \Sigma fv$	4,059 $= \Sigma fv^2$

$$\text{Mean} = \frac{\Sigma fx}{n} = \frac{34,317}{439} = 7,817 \quad \text{or} \quad 6.5 + 0.07817 = 6.5782 \text{ ft}$$

$$\sigma_s = \sqrt{\frac{\Sigma fv^2}{n-1}} = \sqrt{\frac{4,059}{438}} = \sqrt{9.267} = \pm 3.04$$

and since we are here dealing with thousandths of a foot,

$$\sigma_s = \pm 0.00304 \text{ ft} \quad \text{or} \quad \pm 0.0030 \text{ ft} \quad \text{or} \quad \pm 0.003 \text{ ft}$$

This may be called the standard deviation from the mean for any single measurement. Also the *standard error of the mean* is

$$\sigma_m = \frac{\sigma_s}{\sqrt{n}} = \frac{\pm 0.00304}{\sqrt{439}} = \pm 0.00015 \quad \text{or} \quad \pm 0.0002 \text{ ft}$$

4–5 Use of Standard Errors

Standard error is a useful device for comparing different sets of measurements of the same quantity, and is simply illustrated as follows. Suppose that the set of 439 measurements (Art. 4–4) is to be compared with two other sets of measurements of the same value.

Set	n	Mean	Std. Error σ_m
A	439	6.5782	± 0.00015
B	167	6.5784	± 0.00033
C	702	6.5778	± 0.00010

It can be seen that set C has the highest precision and set B the least. If a *best value* is to be found by using all three sets, the middle set should be given the least weight and the last set the greatest weight. Weights are discussed later in Chapter 8.

4–6 Plotting the Histogram and the Probability Curve

The plot of the values from Example 2 of Art. 4–4 is shown in Fig. 6 with $\pm \sigma_s$ ordinates drawn. The histogram (rectangles) has been plotted, and the tops of the rectangles connected by a smooth bell-shaped curve. It is almost the typical probability curve. The probability curve can be described as a continuous curve that applies continuous variables where the difference between one value and the next can be indefinitely small.

Notice, too, that a curve more nearly approaching the bell shape of the probability curve would have resulted if more than 439 values had been used. Mathematically, the curve stretches to infinity in each direction, becoming asymptotic. However, only the small portion shown is important to us.

Plotted on the curve of Fig. 6 are the $\pm \sigma_s$ values, corresponding to actual rod readings of 6.5752 ft and 6.5812 ft. The area beneath the curve between these two ordinates represents the number of observations that fell between these two values. From a quick estimate of the number of values that fall between 6.5752 and 6.5812 (from the frequency distribution table of Example 2 in Art. 4–4), it is seen that about 68% of the values do fall between $+\sigma_s$ and $-\sigma_s$. Further refined analysis, especially of sets of measurements containing many more values, would bear this out. Reference to the Summary Table of Art. 5–13 will indicate that there is a 68.3% certainty that any single value, selected at random from among these measurements of a set, will fall within the $\pm\sigma_s$ range, i.e., be a value that is within ± 0.000304 ft of the mean, 6.5782 ft.

Chapter 5 discusses the probability curve and its meaning as a measure of reliability of measurements.

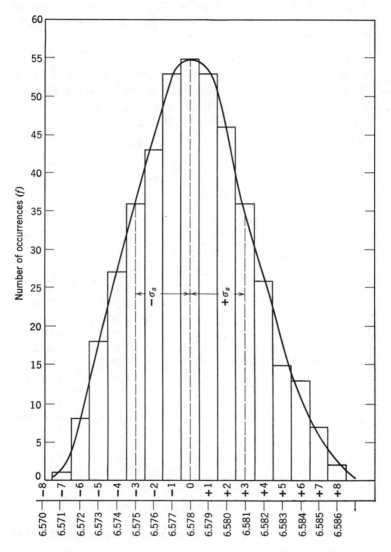

FIGURE 6   Normal probability density curve or frequency density curve.

4–7 Normal Probability Distribution Curve

The bell-shaped curve is the normal probability density curve, but its use as a tool is rather limited. Frequently, a simple variant of this curve can be used, i.e., the normal probability distribution curve. This is given in Appendix F, together with simplified methods of plotting data for a ready visual test of the data on special arithmetic probability paper.

4–8 Short Method for Standard Deviation

For convenience in calculation, the mean may be assumed at the start and corrected later. This method is well adapted to desk calculator, or electronic computer, but is especially useful in manual computation as the following example illustrates.

EXAMPLE. The ages of a group of 15 children are:

$$
\begin{array}{ccccc}
15 & 12 & 11 & 8 & 13 \\
13 & 12 & 8 & 14 & 15 \\
9 & 10 & 12 & 11 & 11
\end{array}
$$

By the usual method:

Age(s)	f	fx	v	v^2	fv^2
8	2	16	−3.6	12.96	25.92
9	1	9	−2.6	6.76	6.76
10	1	10	−1.6	2.56	2.56
11	3	33	−0.6	0.36	1.08
12	3	36	+0.4	0.16	0.48
13	2	26	+1.4	1.96	3.92
14	1	14	+2.4	5.76	5.76
15	2	30	+3.4	11.56	23.12
11.60	15	174			69.60

$$
\therefore \text{Mean} = \frac{\Sigma fv}{\Sigma f} = \frac{174}{15} = 11.60
$$

(from which find v in each case)

$$
\sigma_s = \sqrt{\frac{\Sigma fv^2}{n}} = \sqrt{\frac{69.60}{15}} = \pm 2.15
$$

By the assumed-mean method: Assume that the mean is some middle convenient value, say, 10:

Age	f	v'	fv'	$(v')^2$	$f(v')^2$
8	2	-2	-4	4	8
9	1	-1	-1	1	1
10	1	0	0	0	0
11	3	$+1$	$+3$	1	3
12	3	$+2$	$+6$	4	12
13	2	$+3$	$+6$	9	18
14	1	$+4$	$+4$	16	16
15	2	$+5$	$+10$	25	50
	15		$+24$		108

$$\text{True mean} = \text{Assumed mean} + \frac{\Sigma fv'}{\Sigma f} = 10.00 + \frac{24}{15} = 11.60$$

$$\sigma_s = \sqrt{\frac{\Sigma f(v')^2}{n} - \left(\frac{\Sigma fv'}{\Sigma f}\right)^2} = \sqrt{\frac{108}{15} - 1.60^2}$$

$$= \sqrt{4.64} = \pm 2.15$$

PROBLEMS

1. Of 140 students at camp, the distribution of ages is as given below. Find the standard deviation, the mean, and the standard error of the mean.

17.0— 0	18.0— 8	19.0—5
.1— 1	.1—11	.1—1
.2— 0	.2— 6	.2—0
.3— 1	.3—10	.3—2
.4— 3	.4— 8	.4—6
.5— 8	.5— 7	.5—0
.6— 5	.6— 6	.6—1
.7— 8	.7— 9	.7—0
.8—10	.8— 5	.8—2
.9—14	.9— 3	.9—0

2. Draw the histogram and try to fit a probability curve to it. Then draw in the σ_s, $2\sigma_s$, and $3\sigma_s$ ordinates.

3. From the sets of numbers in Problem 3 of Chapter 3, compute for each set a frequency distribution table, and from that the mean, the standard deviation, the standard error, and the best value of the grouping.

4. A deck of playing cards with all picture cards removed is shuffled and the top card turned up. What is the probability that it is either a 5, a 6, or a 7? (Find σ_s, and then what?)
5. If the population in 1960 is 178,350,000 and that of 1950 was 162,561,000, find that of 1955 by using the (a) arithmetic mean, (b) geometric mean.
6. The following data were obtained from a radar speed detector set up discreetly beside a big city parkway to secure speed information during a free-flowing traffic period. Two different days were used, Tuesday and Wednesday. On the frequency distribution tabulation sheets provided at the back of this book, tally the frequencies, and for each day:

(a) Compute the mean.   (d) Plot the normal probability curve.

(b) Compute the standard deviation.   (e) Plot the normal probability distribution curve.

(c) Compute the standard error.   (f) Plot the data on arithmetic probability paper.

Compare the behavior of traffic on the two days.

Tuesday speeds (mph)

51	58	50	49	42	54	52	49	43	47
52	50	55	47	52	54	49	42	51	50
45	49	47	53	54	40	53	36	50	49
46	51	47	39	47	47	45	48	39	44
48	45	53	51	50	53	55	42	55	48
55	53	54	54	51	47	40	47	45	54
38	50	55	51	52	50	53	44	44	55
43	51	49	33	39	47	48	54	51	53
54	48	47	55	46	45	59	54	47	46
53	44	53	44	46	54	37	43	56	50

Wednesday speeds (mph)

36	53	46	48	53	58	54	42	51	49
49	30	53	48	57	48	44	49	53	41
57	29	57	34	54	52	45	47	44	50
36	51	50	41	41	39	52	36	53	42
47	47	48	41	49	51	46	59	38	49
54	52	46	50	52	47	40	47	40	49
36	38	54	59	46	52	50	52	42	49
41	52	42	50	44	56	36	42	46	45
47	55	54	48	54	45	35	52	43	55
59	52	45	56	60	38	53	54	54	51

five / measures of reliability

5-1 Definitions

A few definitions are now in order, because some terms are frequently used in statistical work and have definite meanings. The number of times a variable occurs in a set of observations is called the *frequency* (f) of the occurrence of the value. A value that represents a series of observations may be the *average*, a term that does not invariably designate the arithmetic mean.

5-2 Mean

The best known and most useful "average" is the *arithmetic mean*, usually referred to as the *mean*; it is calculated by adding all observations and dividing the sum by the total number of observations. In Example 2 of Art. 4–4, the mean is 6.5782 (or 6.578 if rounded off).

5-3 Median

Another "average" often used is the *median*. It is the middle observation, or the arithmetic mean of the two middle observations. The median represents the set of observations in the sense that the number of observations greater than this value is the same as the number that are smaller. In a good, symmetrical set of values, the median will equal the mean. For instance, in a set of 439 observations (Example 2, Art. 4–4) the median will be the 220th value, easily found by counting off 220 values in the f column—provided the values have all been tallied as shown in columnar form. It is 6.578.

5-4 Mode

Another "average" sometimes used is the *mode*, i.e., the most frequently occurring value. In Example 2 of Art. 4–4, the mode is

6.578, since it occurs 55 times, more than any other. If a graph of the frequency distribution is drawn, the mode is the high point or hump of the curve (see Fig. 6). If the curve is symmetrical, it is easily seen that the mode, mean, and median are the same value. But in a curve that is skewed to the right or left, the mode, mean, and median will be somewhat separated. Statistics books give rules-of-thumb for finding each.

5–5 Scatter

The way that the different values lie about this average is called the dispersion or *scatter*, which is, of course, the chief indicator of precision of the set of measurements. Scatter is used to study certainty and uncertainty. Scatter of the values in a set of observations is an indication of their reliability. Wide dispersal bespeaks less reliable data than observations which lie closely about the mean. The shape of the bell curve (the probability curve) gives an indication of scatter: a flat curve would mean greater scatter than a tall narrow curve.

5–6 Range

The simplest measure of scatter is *range*, the distance between the largest and the smallest value. The range of the values in Example 2 of Art. 4–4 is 0.017 ft, the difference between 6.571 and 6.586. However, range is not as indicative of reliability as certain other measures.

5–7 Mean Deviation

More reliable for measuring scatter is *mean deviation* (average error), obtained by adding the individual variations for each value (from any average), and dividing by the number of values. Thus we can have a mean deviation (or mean variation) from the mean, from the median, or from the mode.

In Art. 4–4, Example 2, the sum of the fv column in the tabulation ($\sum fv$) divided by 439(n) gives:

$$\text{Mean deviation} = \frac{\sum fv}{n} = \frac{1,075}{439} = 2.449 \text{ thousandths}$$

Interpreted properly, this shows that ± 0.00245 ft is the average error or the mean variation or deviation from the mean (average) value of the rod readings.

5–8 Standard Deviation

The mean deviation (average error) has a weakness because it tells nothing about the manner in which the values are dispersed. It is possible that one set of measurements may have errors all of medium size, and that another set of measurements may have errors of variable size: several very large, a few medium, and several very small. Yet both sets of measurements may have the same average error. Comparison of the mean deviations of the two sets would give a false indication: in the mean deviations there would be no indication of the distribution (scatter) of the values in each set. There would be no penalty for large errors and no reward for small ones. Fortunately, a better and more universally used measure of scattering is the *standard deviation*. This is, as defined earlier, the square root of the mean of the squares of the deviations (variations) of the observations from their arithmetic mean. It is usually symbolized by small sigma (σ_s), and is also frequently called the *mean square error*.

5–9 The Sigma Error

This error σ_s is used synonymously with "uncertainty" and has been found to be of such size that 68.3% of the errors in the series are less than it and 31.7% are greater. This means that there is a 68.3% certainty that the error of any single measurement will fall between $+\sigma_s$ and $-\sigma_s$. Thus it may be said that a measurement in a series whose deviation from the mean value, either positively or negatively, is greater than σ_s will occur only about 1 in 3 times in the series.

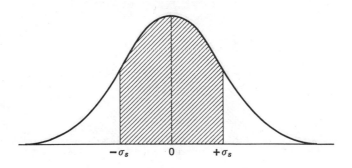

FIGURE 7

It can be seen, therefore, that on the normal probability curve the area contained between the $-\sigma_s$ and the $+\sigma_s$ values of error will amount to 68.3% of the total area. It means that 68.3% of the errors will be plotted between $-\sigma_s$ and $+\sigma_s$, as shown in Fig. 7.

5–10   *The Two-Sigma Error*

Further consideration can show that the area between $-2\sigma_s$ and $+2\sigma_s$ will contain about 95% of the total area. This means that a measurement whose positive or negative deviation from the mean

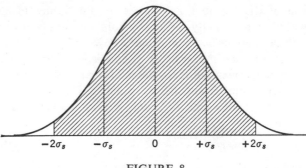

FIGURE 8

value is greater than $2\sigma_s$ will occur only about 1 in 20 times; or $\frac{19}{20}$ of the time the error of a single measurement in the series will fall within $\pm 2\sigma_s$.

5–11   *The Three-Sigma Error*

Finally, the area between $-3\sigma_s$ and $+3\sigma_s$ on the normal probability curve will contain about 99.7% of the total area. This

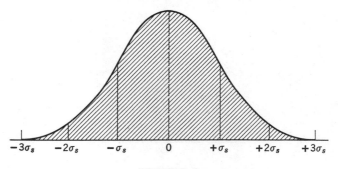

FIGURE 9

means that a measurement whose deviation from the mean value, either positively or negatively, is greater than $3\sigma_s$ will occur only about 1 in 370 times; or 369/370 of the time the error of a single measurement in the series will fall with $\pm 3\sigma_s$.

5–12   *Probable Error*

"Probable error" was once greatly emphasized, but it is being used less and less, mainly because it is defined essentially as a 50% certainty, or 50–50 chance.   On this curve, the probable error is shown by ordinates, between which exactly half of the errors occur.

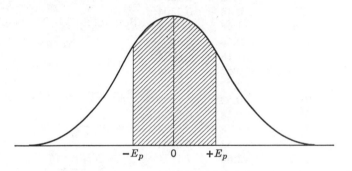

FIGURE 10

The value of the probable error is $0.6745\sigma_s$.   It can be said of any single measurement that its deviation from the mean has an equally good (50–50) chance of being greater or less than the probable error value.   However, fewer and fewer people care to know their chances of the 50–50 occurrence, preferring to know their certainty of being within a known value of the mean on 68% or 95% or 99.5% of their observations.

EXAMPLE.   Here are results of an angle measurement, using an instrument which reads to 1 second of arc (estimated to tenth of second).   Calculate the best value, the mean deviation, and the standard deviation.

Note once again the meaning of "standard error" (Art. 4–3) as an aid to interpreting these results.   We may say of the value of the

Value	v	v^2
19° 27′ 36.2″	0.42	0.1764
34.1	2.52	6.3504
39.7	3.08	9.4864
40.1	3.48	12.1104
36.2	0.42	0.1764
34.1	2.52	6.3504
35.2	1.42	2.0164
35.7	0.92	0.8464
34.9	1.72	2.9584
37.1	0.48	0.2304
38.0	1.38	1.9044
37.2	0.58	0.3364
37.8	1.18	1.3924
36.1	0.52	0.2704
35.9	0.72	0.5184
36.1	0.52	0.2704
36.8	0.18	0.0324
37.9	1.28	1.6384
34.0	2.62	6.8644
39.3	2.68	7.1824
Σ	28.64	61.1120
Mean = 36.62	Σv	Σv^2

Standard deviation:

$$\sigma_s = \sqrt{\frac{\Sigma v^2}{n-1}} = \sqrt{\frac{61.1120}{19}}$$

$$= \sqrt{3.2164} = \pm 01.79''$$

Mean deviation:

$$\bar{v} = \frac{\Sigma v}{n} = \frac{28.64}{20} = 1.43''$$

Best value: 19° 27′ 36.62″

$$2\sigma_s = \pm 03.59''$$
$$3\sigma_s = \pm 05.38''$$

Standard error of mean:

$$\sigma_m = \frac{\sigma_s}{\sqrt{n}}$$

$$= \frac{\pm 01.79}{\sqrt{20}} = \pm 00.40''$$

angle (presuming, of course, that systematic errors have all been eliminated) that:

(a) The most likely value is 19° 27′ 36.62″ as a result of the measurement.

(b) There is a 68.3% certainty that the true value lies between 19° 27′ 36.22″ and 19° 27′ 37.02″ (i.e., $\pm \sigma_m$).

(c) There is a 95.0% certainty that the true value lies between 19° 27′ 35.82″ and 19° 27′ 37.42″ (i.e., $\pm 2\sigma_m$).

(d) There is a 99.7% certainty that the true value lies between 19° 27′ 35.42″ and 19° 27′ 37.82″ (i.e., $\pm 3\sigma_m$).

It might also be noted that the E_p "probable error" (based on

50% certainty) for any single observation is only $0.6745\sigma_s$ ($= \pm 01.21''$) and E_p for the mean value is $0.6745\sigma_m$ ($= \pm 00.28''$). We can say, then, that the *most probable value* of the mean angle (only a 50–50 surety) lies between $19° 27' 36.34''$ and $19° 27' 36.90''$. (The fine expressions "most probable error" and "most probable value"—or simply "probable error" and "probable value"—have been usurped to refer to the 50–50 values. This is correct, but unfortunate. Therefore, whenever we want to designate "sigma error" or "sigma value," we must be careful not to use the word "probable.")

5–13 *Summary Table: Size of Error in any Single Measurement of a Set*

Name of error	Symbol	Value	% Certainty	Probability of larger:
Probable	E_p	$0.6745\sigma_s$	50	1 in 2
Standard deviation	σ_s	$1.0\sigma_s$	68.3	1 in 3
90% error	E_{90}	$1.6449\sigma_s$	90	1 in 10
Two-sigma, or 95% error	$2\sigma_s$	$2\sigma_s$ $3E_p$	95	1 in 20
Three-sigma	$3\sigma_s$	$3\sigma_s$	99.7	1 in 370
Maximum*	E_{max}	$3.29\sigma_s$	99.9$^+$	1 in 1,000

* Some authorities regard the 95% error as the "maximum error." Neither view is absolutely correct, since the theoretical maximum error is $\pm \infty$, which does not occur in practice. It is, then, a good practical decision to use the 95% or the 99$^+$% error as the "practical" maximum tolerable.

From \ To	50.0% E_p	68.3% σ	90.0% E_{90}	95.0% 2σ	99.7% 3σ	99.9+% E_{max}
E_p	1.000	1.483	2.439	2.961	4.449	4.879
σ	0.674	1.000	1.645	2.000	3.000	3.290
E_{90}	0.410	0.608	1.000	1.215	1.824	2.000
2σ	0.337	0.500	0.822	1.000	1.500	1.645
3σ	0.224	0.333	0.548	0.666	1.000	1.096
E_{max}	0.205	0.304	0.500	0.608	0.912	1.000

EXAMPLE. If a probable error (50%) is known to be ± 1.927 mph in a speed reading of 100 mph, find the Standard deviation (68.3%).

$$\sigma_s = \pm 1.927(1.483) = \pm 2.855 \text{ mph}$$

PROBLEMS

1. The weather reporters frequently say something like this: "We're running four degrees below the normal mean for this date. The temperature is now 47°; the high was 52° at 2 P.M. and the low was 35° at 12 minutes after 7 this morning." Explain the several implications of the statement, such as how the mean is computed, telling what is the normal mean for the date, etc.
2. Test the σ_s, $2\sigma_s$, $3\sigma_s$ values against the data of the second example of Art. 4–4, seeking to ascertain if the proper percentage inclusions are borne out. Discuss any lack of conformity thereto.
3. For Problem 1 of Chapter 4, find the median and the mode.
4. In the example of Art. 5–13, find the median and the mode.
5. If the probable error of a length is ± 0.0764 yd, what is the 3σ error? The 90% error? The "maximum" error?
6. The harmonic mean, not mentioned in the text, is useful for averaging speeds. It is expressed thus:

$$M_{\text{Harm.}} = \frac{n}{[\sum 1/x]}$$

If an automobile travels around a one-mile square, the first leg at 40 mph, the second at 30 mph, the third at 20 mph, and the fourth at

10 mph, what is its average speed as computed thus? (Let $x =$ speed, $n =$ number of sides in this case.) Compare this with the "average" speed as computed by the arithmetic mean.

In testing gyroscope guidance systems of missiles, the true meridian must be known. The Hughes Aircraft Company uses Kern DKM 2 theodolites with autocollimating eyepieces for determining the meridian and for transferring direction to the guidance system. (Photo courtesy Hughes Aircraft Company, El Segundo, Calif.)

six / reliability of repeated measurements

6-1 Multiple Measurements

From the foregoing treatment of the sigma error (standard deviation) it is apparent that multiple measurements must be made of any quantity if anything is to be known about the precision (and, consequently, the accuracy) of the measurement.   Frequently, a second or check measurement is made by careful individuals, a sort of "look-twice-and-be-sure" response.   The question then arises: How many measurements must be made to achieve an acceptable precision?

Although it is sometimes specified that the standard deviation of a single value (σ_s) or the standard error of the mean (σ_m) shall not exceed a certain size, many times it is specified by fixing the number of times some observations must be made.   In still other instances, the engineer must make his own determination of how precise to be and how many times to measure.

6-2 Number of Repeated Measurements

If we examine the equation for standard deviation, we see that it is essentially

$$\sigma_s = \sqrt{\frac{\sum v^2}{n-1}} = \frac{K}{\sqrt{n-1}}$$

where K may be assumed to remain fixed for the given series of measurements.   Plotting this general form of the equation (considering K invariant), we get a curve as shown in Fig. 11.   Note

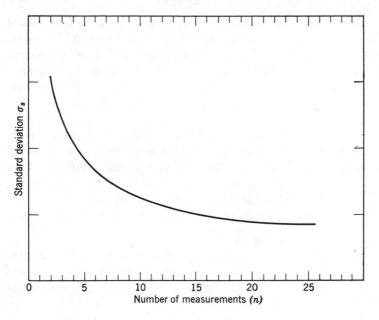

FIGURE 11

that essentially the same results will ensue if the slightly erroneous form $\sigma_s = K/\sqrt{n}$ is plotted.

By examination of the curve, we discover that the value of σ_s is seen to get better (i.e., decrease) only slightly with the adding of more measurements beyond about 10 or 15. It is not ordinarily justifiable, therefore, to repeat measurements beyond 15 or so for the purpose of reducing the uncertainty of the arithmetic mean.

6–3   *Rejecting Measurements*

Occasionally, when examining a set of measured values, some individual measurement may differ so widely from others in the same set that we suspect the discrepancy may be due to a mistake. If the widely divergent value is retained, it will produce a marked effect upon the value of the arithmetic mean and its standard deviation, which represent the whole set of measurements. In such a case it may be well to exclude this measurement from the set.

The criterion and procedure for rejecting measurements are based on the principle that the range $\pm\sigma_s$ embraces 68.3% of the errors, $\pm 2\sigma_s$ embraces 95.0% of the errors, $\pm 3\sigma_s$ embraces 99.7% of the errors, and that $\pm 3.29\sigma_s$ embraces about 99.9% of the errors. Hence, the probability of making an error greater than $3.29\sigma_s$ is only about 1 in 1,000, and we may safely assume that apparent error of much greater than that magnitude must be a mistake.

Thus, if a "wild" value is found in a set of measurements, compute the arithmetic mean by using the "wild" value, and find the σ_s. Next, discover $3.29\sigma_s$ and discard from the mean value the suspected "wild" value(s) that lie beyond this amount. Then recompute the entire set, using only the good values. (Sometimes a simple inspection initially will enable us to discard a "way out" reading.) Check the example before Art. 5–13 for "wild" values.

6–4 *Maximum Possible Error*

Consideration of the "maximum" error likely to occur in a set of measurements brings to light an extremely important reason why multiple measurements are made of any given quantity. Such repeated measurements assure us that we are within a definite range of the "true" value. The maximum error $(\pm 3.29\sigma_s)$ can be computed and used as a measure of the correctness of other check values obtained.

For example, in a given set of 20 measurements of a fluid flow in a pipe, the quantity (Q) is found to be 0.817 cfs (cu ft/sec) with a σ_s of ± 0.0025. By another single measurement the Q is determined to be 0.829 cfs, and the question of its validity is raised. The maximum error $(3.29\sigma_s)$ likely to occur is ± 0.0082, causing us to have no confidence in any value outside the range 0.809 to 0.825. Thus we suspect that the value 0.829 contains a mistake, or that it has not been corrected for some systematic error(s), or that the method used to determine it is suspect.

6–5 *Use of Maximum Error*

Throughout measurements, the "maximum" error $(3.29\sigma_s)$ must be used as a criterion in any operation that requires "exactness." Placing a bridge pier a half-mile out in open water by measurements from shore, for instance, must be sure and certain. The distance and angles used to compute the over-water lengths and establish the pier coordinates must have a known maximum error within an established tolerance. It will not suffice to know that we are probably (50–50 chance) correct within ±0.005 ft, or even 68.3% certain.   In this case, the 99.9$^+$% is most likely required.

6–6   *Significance*

The foregoing brings to light the concept of "significance" in statistical work.   The term "significance" is used to indicate that the odds are heavy against the deviation from its expected value for something occurring by chance as a result of random sampling.   In practice, odds of 19 to 1 against an occurrence by chance are taken as indicating that the occurrence is "significant."   Some prefer heavier odds, such as 99 to 1, before conceding that some happening has significance, but in general a probability of 19 to 1 is used as standard.   The 19 to 1 corresponds roughly to the odds of getting a deviation from the mean of a normal distribution greater than twice the standard deviation, either positively or negatively.

6–7   *Using the Standard Error to Compare Sets*

The standard error (σ_m) is useful when comparing the mean values of two or more different sets of measurements.   In the earlier example involving 20 measurements of an angle (Example in Art. 5–12), it is obvious that an entirely different 20 results might have been obtained, even by the same observer at the same time under identical conditions.   We assume, knowing no better, that the 20 values recorded represent a good distribution, making a good bell-shaped curve.   It may well be that the set of 20 is a trifle skewed to right or to left, however, and the mean will to some extent be affected.   This was not checked by plotting to discover any skew, though this might be done.

Assume next that another set of 20 observations is made, this set having a different skew (perhaps) and a different mean.   The following question can then be validly asked: Are these two means significantly different?   In other words, of all the hundreds and hundreds of possible observational values, the 40 here recorded are only two sets of random samples.   And the two means of the two samples will be distributed with a standard error normally, meaning that the observed mean should be distributed about the "true" mean in a normal fashion.

6–8   *Standard Error of the Differences between Means*

By computing the standard errors—one for each set—and comparing the two, we can discover if their respective mean values differ significantly from each other. We can do so simply by computing the *standard error of the difference between the means* by this formula:

$$\sigma_{diff.} = \sqrt{[\sigma^2]_A + [\sigma^2]_B}$$

We then observe the agreement between the $\sigma_{diff.}$ and the actual difference between the mean values. If the actual difference between the two means is greater than twice this value (i.e., $d > 2\sigma_{diff.}$), then they are significantly different values. This indicates that it is unlikely (beyond a 19 to 1 chance) that the means represent the same measurement or the same measuring conditions. The derivation of this formula is beyond the scope of this text.

EXAMPLE. Two sets of measurements of angles are made, each consisting of 20 measurements. The mean and the standard error of each have been computed. Determine if these two means are significantly different.

Set	Mean value	n	σ_m	σ_m^2
A	19° 27′ 36.12″	20	± 0.42″	0.1764
B	19° 27′ 34.92″	20	± 0.67″	0.4489
Diff.	01.20″			

The standard error of difference between A and B is:

$$\sigma_{diff.} = \pm \sqrt{0.1764 + 0.4489}$$
$$= \pm \sqrt{0.6253} = \pm 0.79″$$
$$2\sigma_{diff.} = \pm 1.58″$$

Comparison of this with the difference between the two means above (1.20″) indicates that these two sets do validly represent the value, and that either mean can be used as "best" value of the quantity measured. (In fact, these two mean values could be averaged together to get a "best" value by a "weighted mean" computation, as discussed in Chapter 8.)

EXAMPLE. A base line is measured several times by each of two different parties under different climatic circumstances, with different (but standardized) tapes, but with methods of the same order of precision. Comparison of results shows:

$$\begin{array}{cc} A & B \\ \text{Value} \quad 1{,}819.127 \text{ meters} & 1{,}819.210 \text{ meters} \\ \sigma_m = 0.019 \text{ meters} & \sigma_m = 0.031 \text{ meters} \end{array}$$

$$\sigma_{\text{diff.}} = \sqrt{0.019^2 + 0.031^2} = \sqrt{0.001324}$$
$$= \pm 0.036$$
$$2\sigma_{\text{diff.}} = \pm 0.072 \text{ meter}$$
$$1{,}819.210 - 1{,}819.127 = 0.083 \text{ meter}$$

It should be concluded that there exists a significant difference between the two results, being more than a chance deviation (expected 1 in 20 times). A difference of more than $2\sigma_{\text{diff.}}$ occurs too infrequently by chance (i.e., by random fluctuation) to be written off as caused by random errors.

6-9 Limitation of Standard Error

Note here that the formula for $\sigma_{\text{diff.}}$ cannot, strictly speaking, be validly used for comparison purposes unless there are a large number of measurements, say about 50 in all. This would be clear if the expression had been derived. For practical purposes, however, it can be used with proper caution as an indicator of sameness if fewer than 50 measurements comprise each set.

PROBLEMS

1. A survey of the ages of 100 of the 150 students in a class was made by one person, and a similar survey of 60 of the 150 was made independently by another person:

Mean $A = 16.87 \pm 0.24$ Mean $B = 17.19 \pm 0.31$

The standard errors of the mean are given.
(a) What is the standard deviation in each set?
(b) How can it be reasonably established that these two surveys were made of the same group (population)?

2. The following data represent measurements of machine shafts taken from production at random, presumably thus representing the entire production. What is the average diameter of the shaft and what is the maximum tolerance that must be established if 95% of the shafts are to be acceptable? What degree of precision does this represent?

2.0001	2.0000	1.9999	2.0000
2.0002	2.0000	1.9998	2.0000
2.0001	2.0003	1.9999	1.9997
2.0002	2.0000	1.9998	2.0000
2.0001	2.0001	1.9999	1.9999

3. Around 1950, by using Geodimeters, Bergstrand computed the velocity of infrared light to be 299,793.1 ± 0.25 km/sec and Aslakson independently computed it to be 299,792.4 ± 2.4 km/sec. Determine whether these two values are significantly different.
4. Shortly thereafter Aslakson, using other equipment, computed the velocity of radio waves to be 299,794.2 ± 1.4 km/sec. Is the velocity of radio waves significantly different from that of light waves?

seven / propagation of errors in computing

7-1 Remarks

When using direct measurement values to compute final results, such as to reach indirect measurements, it is necessary to guard against carrying excessive random error into the result. Thus it is necessary to know the size of the error in the result after performing arithmetic operations on any measured value or on the mean of several values. The general rules of error propagation refer to σ_s, σ_m, E_p, or any similar random errors. (In the following operations, the error of the mean is generally used, though the subscript m is omitted for clarity.)

7-2 Addition of Values Containing Errors

According to the laws of probability, when quantities are added, each containing an error (σ, E_p, 2σ, or any similar accidental type), their sum contains an error equal to the square root of sum of the squares of the errors of the added quantities. Thus,

$$E_{\text{sum}} = \sqrt{E_1{}^2 + E_2{}^2 + E_3{}^2 + \cdots + E_n{}^2}$$

For example, if line $ABCD$ is comprised of three measured segments, each value given being the mean of many measurements:

$$AB = 107.162 \pm 0.002 \text{ in.}$$
$$BC = 491.043 \pm 0.010$$
$$CD = 216.191 + 0.005$$

$$AD = 814.396 \pm \sqrt{0.002^2 + 0.010^2 + 0.005^2}$$
$$= 814.396 \pm 0.011 \text{ in.}$$

While this is a valid rule to follow in sums of quantities affected by errors, some authorities insist that the *maximum* error in the sum of the three quantities is $\pm(0.002 + 0.010 + 0.005) = \pm 0.017$ in. They say (safely enough) that "the error in the sum is not greater than the sum of the errors in the added quantities."

Of course, the validity of this "maximum" error is unquestionable, but it is not reasonable to insist on such certitude because each of the three segment values is the mean of several readings, and each is labeled with an error value signifying a reasonable uncertainty. It is very unlikely that each of the quantities is uncertain by the maximum amount shown *and* each in the same direction at the same time, *all* being either too small or too large. More likely, the measured quantities will differ from their true values by less than the indicated value of the uncertainties, with some plus and others minus. Thus the possible error in a sum (or other calculated quantity) is much more logically represented by a probable than by an absolute value. Hence, we shall use the generally accepted probability-type square-root computation for the error in a sum.

7–3 Subtraction of Values Containing Errors

If we agree that subtraction is the addition of one positive and one negative value, the error of the result can be seen to be validly computed in the same manner as the addition error:

$$E_{\text{diff.}} = \pm \sqrt{E_1{}^2 + E_2{}^2}$$

For example, in subtraction of two angular values:

$$\begin{aligned}
\text{Angle } AOC &= 87° \, 45' \, 15'' \pm 05'' \\
-\text{Angle } BOC &= 41° \, 53' \, 50'' \pm 10''
\end{aligned}$$

$$\overline{\text{Angle } AOB = 45° \, 51' \, 25'' \pm \sqrt{05^2 + 10^2} = \pm 11.2''}$$

7–4 Multiplication of Values Containing Errors

In multiplying two quantities that contain errors, this is the general form:

$$(A + E_A)(B \pm E_B) = AB \pm E_A B \pm E_B A \pm E_A E_B$$

To neglect the last term is not serious, since both factors are extremely small. Hence, it may be seen that (from the previous rule for addition of errors):

$$E_{\text{product}} = \pm \sqrt{(E_A B)^2 + (E_B A)^2} = AB \sqrt{\frac{(E_A B)^2 + (E_B A)^2}{A^2 B^2}}$$

$$= \pm AB \sqrt{\left(\frac{E_A}{A}\right)^2 + \left(\frac{E_B}{B}\right)^2} \qquad \text{(General form)}$$

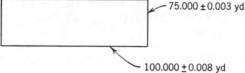

75.000 ± 0.003 yd

100.000 ± 0.008 yd

Thus, if we compute the area of the rectangle shown:

$$A = 7{,}500.00 \pm \text{error}$$
$$\text{Error} = \pm \sqrt{(100 \times 0.003)^2 + (75.0 \times 0.008)^2}$$
$$= \pm \sqrt{0.0900 + 0.3600} = \pm \sqrt{0.4500} = \pm 0.67 \ \text{yd}^2$$

The best value = $7{,}500.00 \pm 0.67 \ \text{yd}^2$.

Similarly, the product of several factors has this error:

$$E_{\text{product}} = \pm ABC \ldots N \sqrt{\left(\frac{E_A}{A}\right)^2 + \left(\frac{E_B}{B}\right)^2 + \left(\frac{E_C}{C}\right)^2 + \cdots + \left(\frac{E_N}{N}\right)^2}$$

$$\text{(General form)}$$

Each fraction under the radical may be called the "relative error" of the designated factor, or percentage error.

7–5 Division of Values Containing Errors

Though the derivation is beyond the scope of this treatment, the error in a quotient $(A \pm E_A) \div (B \pm E_B)$ is:

$$E_{\text{quotient}} = \frac{A}{B} \sqrt{\left(\frac{E_A}{A}\right)^2 + \left(\frac{E_B}{B}\right)^2}$$

or, written in another form:

$$E_{\text{quotient}} = \frac{1}{B^2} \sqrt{(E_A B)^2 + (E_B A)^2}$$

Thus, in a given case where it is desired to stake out a rectangular plot *PQRS* for a building whose area must be 200.000 ± 0.165 ft² and whose one fixed dimension necessarily is 10.000 ± 0.008 ft, the perpendicular dimension is

$$PQ = \frac{200.000}{10.000} \pm E_{\text{quotient}}$$

$$= 20.000 \pm \frac{200.000}{10.000} \sqrt{\left(\frac{0.165}{200.000}\right)^2 + \left(\frac{0.008}{10.000}\right)^2}$$

$$= 20.000 \pm 20.000 \sqrt{68 \times 10^{-8} + 64 \times 10^{-8}}$$

$$= 20.000 \pm 20.000 \,(11.5 \times 10^{-4})$$

$$= 20.000 \pm 0.023 \text{ ft}$$

7–6 *Multiplication of Values Containing Errors by a Constant (Exact Number)*

Conversion of a measured value into other units is often encountered, or totaling the measured value a number of times. The value of the product $C(A \pm E_A)$ is seen to be $CA \pm CE_A$, and:

$$E_{\text{product}} = \pm CE_A$$

Hence, for example, if a length is measured as 3,612.28 ft ± 0.12 and to compute another result it is multiplied by

$$\frac{\sin 90° \, 00' \, 00''}{\sin 39° \, 51' \, 32''} = \frac{1.00000000}{0.62740449} = 0.15938681$$

$$\text{The product} = 575.750 \pm 0.15938681 \times (0.12)$$

$$= 575.750 \pm 0.191 \text{ ft}$$

Similarly, to convert 802.316 ± 0.027 meters to feet, the proper value in feet is:

$$\text{Product} = 802.316(3.2808333) \pm 0.027(3.2808)$$

$$= 2,632.265 \pm 0.089 \text{ ft}$$

(The product here, incidentally, may properly be given to seven significant figures, since the *8* in 802.316 is practically *two* significant figures, being very nearly *10*.)

7–7 *Elevation to a Power of a Quantity Containing an Error*

If we regard the raising to the nth power to be simply a multiplying of a quantity by itself n times $(A + E_A)^n$, then the error of the result would seem to be, as ascertained from the general form for a product (see Art. 7–4 above):

$$E_{\text{power}} = A^n\sqrt{n(E_A/A)^2} = \frac{E_A}{A} A^n\sqrt{n}$$

$$= E_A A^{n-1}\sqrt{n}$$

Our assumption would imply, however, that the E_A value is not fixed for the quantity A but may be different in value each time that A is used. Such is not the case, since the quantity A has a fixed value and a fixed E_A throughout. Hence, once the measurement of A is completed, the error E_A is fixed and will not vary so as to compensate or tend to compensate. Hence, the correct evaluation can be made of E_{power} if we note that error E_A will be involved n times and not $\sqrt{n}$ times. Thus, correctly:

$$E_{\text{power}} = nA^n\sqrt{[E_A/A]^2} = nA^{n-1}E_A$$

EXAMPLE. If a perfect cube of silicon crystal is measured by a micrometer microscope to be 4.00 ± 0.02 micron, its volume is

$$64.0 \pm (3 \times 4.00^2 \times 0.02) = 27.0 \pm 0.96 \text{ micron}^3$$

The implication is that the cube is measured along one edge only, and the assumption of perfect cubical shape is made.

EXAMPLE. Find the error in the volume of a sphere whose diameter is repeatedly measured and found to be 4.000 ± 0.006 in. Let

$$A = \text{radius} = 2.000$$
$$E_A = \pm 0.003$$

$$\text{Volume of the sphere} = \tfrac{4}{3}\pi(2.000)^3$$
$$= 33.510 \text{ cu in.}$$

$$\text{Error of Volume} = \tfrac{4}{3}\pi[3(2.000)^2(0.003)]$$
$$= \pm 0.048\pi$$
$$= \pm 0.151 \text{ cu in.}$$

7–8 Root of Quantity Containing an Error

If we consider the problem to be $(A \pm E_A)^{1/n}$, by using the preceding equation:

$$E_{\text{root}} = \frac{1}{n} E_A A^{1/n-1} = \frac{E_A \sqrt[n]{A}}{nA}$$

Thus, if a true square must be measured out such that its area is 16.000 ± 0.008, the length of each side must be:

$$L = 16.000 \pm \frac{0.008\sqrt{16.000}}{2 \times 16.000}$$

$$= 4.000 \pm 0.001$$

7–9 Other Operations

The foregoing principles are basic in the study of calculations which involve quantities containing errors, but certain frequently used concepts should be restated here for emphasis.

(a) The error of the mean of a series of measurements is found, from principles of Arts. 7–2 and 7–5 above, thus:

$$\text{Mean} = \frac{(A_1 + A_2 + A_3 + \cdots + A_n) \pm \sqrt{v_1{}^2 + v_2{}^2 + v_3{}^2 + \cdots + v_n{}^2}}{n}$$

$$= A_{\text{mean}} \pm \frac{\sqrt{\sum v^2}}{n}$$

But

$$\sqrt{\frac{\sum v^2}{(n-1)}} = \sigma_s = \sqrt{\frac{\sum v^2}{n}} \quad \text{(approximately)}$$

$$\therefore \quad \sigma_m = \frac{\sigma_s}{\sqrt{n}}$$

(b) The addition of quantities having the same size of errors (see Art. 7–2) can be represented thus:

$$(A \pm E_1) + (B \pm E_1) + (C \pm E_1) + \cdots + (N \pm E_1)$$

$$= (A + B + C + \cdots + N) \pm \sqrt{E_1{}^2 + E_1{}^2 + E_1{}^2 + \cdots + E_n{}^2}$$

$$= (A + B + C + \cdots + N) \pm E_1\sqrt{n}$$

For example, if a 300-ft tape has been corrected for all its systematic errors but has (necessarily) some accidental errors affecting it and its use, and the net accidental error (E) is figured to be ± 0.024 ft, what is the error likely in a distance of 1,545.0 ft? Since $\frac{1545}{300} = 5.030$,

$$E_{1545} = \pm 0.024\sqrt{5.030} = \pm 0.054 \text{ ft}$$

PROBLEMS

1. A right angle AOB is set off from line OA, and point B is set at a distance of exactly 200 ft. If the angle is sure to within $\pm 01''$, how certain is point B? (Show by enlarged sketch.)

2. Compute the uncertainty (again using sketch) in the case of Problem 1 if this time the distance OB is 200.000 ft $\pm$ 0.008 ft (i.e., maximum error).

3. Three segments of a line AB are measured several times and the mean of each set is given, along with standard error (σ_m):

$$
\begin{aligned}
&1.\ 461.812 \pm 0.027 \\
&2.\ 201.003 \pm 0.009 \\
&3.\ \ \ 91.161 \pm 0.002
\end{aligned}
$$

Find the sum and its standard error.

4. The area of a right triangle is to be computed by its base and altitude:

$$
\begin{aligned}
\text{Base} \quad &410.817 \pm 0.050 \quad (2\sigma_m \text{ error}) \\
\text{Alt.} \quad &101.326 \pm 0.025 \quad (2\sigma_m \text{ error})
\end{aligned}
$$

Find the area and its $2\sigma_m$ error.

5. A distance AB is measured as 1,427.28 ft $\pm$ 0.52 ft along a bearing of N 45° 00′ 00.0″ E $\pm$ 15″. If the coordinates of A are fixed as N 6,792.14 and E 11,792.62, find:

   (a) The coordinates of B.
   (b) The error in northing (latitude) of the course AB.
   (c) The error in easting (departure) of the course AB.

   (*Hint*: See Appendix A before fixing upon the square root of 2 for use in this problem.)

eight / errors and weights

8-1 Weight and Reliability

A further and more common use of the standard error (σ_m) is to assign weights to measurement values which are to be added, averaged, or otherwise utilized in computation. Among the means of several sets of measurements, weights can be used to distinguish which are the more reliable and how much more reliable they are. Weights can also be used to grade the sets by some numerical system as to the reliability of each. Assigning a weight to each set will allow each set to exert its proper influence in computations based on measurements.

8-2 The Weighted Mean

The "average" of the means of several sets of measurements that will give correct cognizance to the influence that each should play in determination of the true value is known as the *weighted mean*. It is the only logical key to combining means of several sets, and is computed by simply multiplying each measurement value v by its

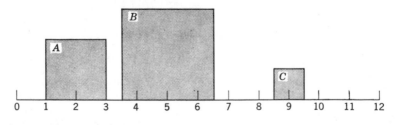

properly assigned weight factor w, then dividing the sum of the products by the sum of the weights:

$$\overline{M} = \frac{\sum (v \cdot w)}{\sum w}$$

This is analogous to the "first moment" principle, as exemplified by the problem of finding the location of the center of gravity of three cubes on a board (where volume is a "weight factor"):

Cube	Vol.	x	Vx
A	4	2	8
B	9	5	45
C	1	9	9
$\sum$	14		62

$$\bar{x} = \frac{\sum Vx}{\sum V} = \frac{62}{14} = 4.43 \text{ in.}$$

This indicates the board would balance if a pivot were placed at 4.43 in., the center of gravity (centroid) of all the volumes.

8–3 *Assigning Weights*

In determining the weights to be assigned to measured quantities, various guides are used as reasonable indicators, ranging from simple judgment to "exact" statistical computation. Besides certain general rules for assigning weights, three simple notions which are commonly used should be mentioned:

Use of Judgment. Sometimes the judgment of the measurer must play a major role in assigning importance to measurements. For example, we may have ascertained the velocity of the maximum wind in a hurricane by using two different instruments stationed $1\frac{1}{2}$ miles apart, but one of the instruments was later blown over by the wind. The observer may remember doubting the value of its readings and, because the destroyed instrument is now unavailable for testing, would correctly discount much of the worth of this recording. It may be his judgment that only one-tenth as much weight should be accorded to its reading, thus:

Instrument	Max. veloc. (v)	Wt. (w)	vw
A	87 mph	10	870
B (destroyed)	81 mph	1	81
Σ		11	951

Estimated mean = $86\frac{1}{2}$ mph

Often in engineering, judgment is also required in locating a factory when two or more sites may offer varying degrees of similar advantages. Price of land, labor market, transportation difficulty, raw material availability, nearness of product market, transportation, etc., are accorded arbitrary or rational weight factors for each site to facilitate the comparison.

Use of Indexes. Often devices for assigning weights are available, as is illustrated in the following comparison that uses the "index" of the dollar to assign weights for a cost problem:

Year	Cost of typewriter (c)	Worth of the dollar (w) (1940 = 1.00)	Comparable 1940 costs (c/w)	Comparable 1960 costs $\left(\dfrac{c}{w} \times \dfrac{1.82}{1.00}\right)$	Costs × dollar worth
1940	$115	1.00	$115	$210	115
1950	$157	1.49	$105	$191	234
1960	$203	1.82	$112	$202	370
Σ		4.31			719

Here it is seen that the dollar "index" (compare "cost-of-living index") is used as a weight factor to compare costs. The weighted mean cost of a typewriter during two decades (for whatever good it might do) is also:

$$\overline{M} = \frac{719}{4.31} = \$166$$

although this is not really in terms of any one year's dollar and serves no real purpose in a comparison. (The valuable comparable costs occur in the tabulation.)

Concept of Numbers. Another weighting device is the concept of number. For instance, if three clocks say 3 o'clock, we reason that it is more reliably 3 o'clock than if only one clock says so. Or if five people state that such and such an event happened, it gains credence. Note that these should be, in all such cases, independent observations. We have three independent judges at the end of a race, for instance, and three independent timers. The three "times" of the race may be given equal weight because the people are considered equally responsive and all other conditions are approximately equivalent.

GENERAL RULES FOR ASSIGNING WEIGHTS

8–4 *Equal Weights*

When the same conditions prevail, equal weights can be assigned to two measurements of the same quantity, or to two sets of measurements of the same quantity.

EXAMPLE. A distance PQ was measured six times by team A and six times by team B, each team using identical equipment and care. Their results must be accorded equal weight, thus:

Team	Value	Weight	vw
A	15.6172 m	1	15.6172
B	15.6184 m	1	15.6184
Σ		2	31.2356

$$\overline{M} = \frac{31.2356}{2} = 15.6178 \text{ m}$$

This is, of course, to take the simple arithmetic mean, which is a special case of the weighted mean (when weights are equal.)

A variation of this equal-weight principle is illustrated by adding the means of two measured values (achieved under identical conditions) to get a sum. For example, angle AOB (30° 13' 42") is added to angle BOC (15° 49' 50") to give angle AOC ($= 46° 03' 32"$). There is nothing else that can be done, since we do not have a check value for the sum. This becomes clearer from the next article.

8–5 *Equal Weights, with Exact Check Value*

In a given instance where a sum of three equal-weight mean values must equal a fixed value, adjustment can be made equally to each mean so that the sum of the parts exactly equals the whole. For example, if each of the three angles of a triangle are measured several times, their mean values when added must equal (or else be adjusted to) 180° exactly. Here is such a situation:

Angle	Observed mean value	Weight	Adjustment (02.7 ÷ 3)	Adjusted values
A	49° 46' 45.7"	1	+ 00.9"	49° 46' 46.6"
B	34° 51' 39.8"	1	+ 00.9"	34° 51' 40.7"
C	95° 21' 31.8"	1	+ 00.9"	95° 21' 32.7"
Σ	179° 59' 57.3"		+ 02.7"	180° 00' 00.0"

Note that the exactly fixed value (180° 00' 00.0") can be considered to have "infinite" weight and thus zero adjustment.

Similar situations arise when angular values of any polygon are measured, when angles around a point are measured to "close the horizon," etc. However, measurements that can be checked against exact values are not very frequent.

8–6 *Equal Weights, with Arbitrary Check Value*

It may happen, however, that a "total" or a check value may be fixed merely for convenience, or to preclude continuing endless minor adjustments of its value. For example, a property line fixed by monuments, set once as 891.750 ft long, is now measured in two segments that do not total exactly that distance. Adjustment of the segments is made, once it is seen that they total very nearly that value. The mode of adjustment here is that of "prorating" the discrepancy on the basis of segment lengths, assuming that any errors are proportional to the lengths. (The reason for the method of prorating does not follow from this present treatment but comes instead from an understanding of how errors are made in taping.)

Segment	Value	Weight	Adjustment	Adjusted value
1	216.502	1	$\dfrac{216.5}{891.8} \times 0.011 = 0.0027$	216.499
2	675.259	1	$\dfrac{675.3}{891.8} \times 0.011 = 0.0083$	675.251
Σ	891.761		0.011	891.750
Fixed	891.750			

8–7 *Equal Weights of Component and Total*

More frequently, instead of an exact total against which to check, the only available value for the total is a measured value. Here is what is equivalent to a case of three equally weighted measurements and a total—the equivalent of four weighted measurements, with adjustment made on all components and on the total. For example, lengths are measured:

Segment	Value	Weight	Adjustment	Adjusted value
AB	15.4179	1	+0.00553	15.4234
BC	8.0124	1	+0.00287	8.0153
CD	20.6008	1	+0.00738	20.6082
Σ	(44.0311)			(44.0469)
AD	44.0627	1	−0.01577	44.0469
Diff.	0.0316			0.0000

Prorating here can best be done by considering that the measured distance is twice the total length (i.e., a round trip). The adjustments are, for the above tabulation:

$$\frac{15.4179}{(44.0627 + 44.0311)} \times 0.0316 = 0.00553, \text{ etc. (including } AD)$$

8–8   *Weights Proportional to Number of Measurements*

When conditions are identical except that one quantity is measured more times than another, weights are reasonably assigned in proportion to the number of measurements. Thus, length *BC* is measured by Shoran five times in one set and three times in another with these resulting means:

Set	No. of measurements	Value (miles)	Weight	*wv*
1	5	187.23	1.667	312.056
2	3	187.16	1	187.160
Σ			2.667	499.216

$$\overline{M} = \frac{499.216}{2.667} = 187.206 \text{ miles}$$

This notion is not to be confused with that used in computing the arithmetic mean from a frequency table (see Art. 4–4). The assigning of weights in this present instance has nothing to do with the magnitude of the values found, only with the effort expended.

8–9   *Weights and Errors*

Because the standard error (σ_m) of a set of measurements signifies the degree of uncertainty (and, therefore, certainty), it furnishes a guide to the weight we may accord the mean of a set. A large standard error, induced by large dispersion and, mainly, by too few measurements in a set, indicates that the set should be regarded as less certain than a set with a small standard error. Therefore, the set with the larger standard error should be accorded less weight, and the set with the smaller error more weight.

8–10 Weights and the Standard Error

From the definition of standard error,

$$\sigma_m = \frac{\sigma_s}{\sqrt{n}}$$

it can be seen that the error varies inversely with the square root of the number of observations or, stated differently, the number of observations varies inversely with the square of the standard error. Because weights ought to be assigned to sets in proportion to the number of measurements in the sets, weights ought to be varied according to the inverse square of the standard errors of the sets, or

$$W_1 : W_2 : W_3 : \text{etc.} = \frac{1}{(\sigma_m{}^2)_1} : \frac{1}{(\sigma_m{}^2)_2} : \frac{1}{(\sigma_m{}^2)_3} : \text{etc.}$$

If, for example, the stress in the steel wall of a high-pressure cylinder under load is recorded in four sets of measurements by strain gages, each set being of different uncertainty, the weighted mean can be found.

Set	Stress (psi)	σ_m	Weight ratio	Weight factor	vw
A	39,765	± 125	$(1/125)^2 = 6.39 \times 10^{-5}$	1.54	61,238.1
B	39,810	± 80	$(1/80)^2 = 15.7 \times 10^{-5}$	3.77	150,083.7
C	39,716	± 155	$(1/155)^2 = 4.16 \times 10^{-5}$	1.00	39,716.0
D	39,791	± 140	$(1/140)^2 = 5.10 \times 10^{-5}$	1.23	48,942.9
Σ				7.54	299,980.7

$$\text{Weighted mean } (\overline{M}) = \frac{299,980.7}{7.54} = 39,785.2 \text{ psi}$$

Note that the value with the smallest standard error is given the greatest influence in fixing the value of the weighted mean.

8–11 Weights and Adjustments

Since weights signify the degree of reliability of measurement sets, it is apparent that a value with a high weight factor is not to be greatly adjusted (some would say "corrected") and, conversely, a value with a low weight factor should be adjusted more. Therefore, the adjustment ("corrections," loosely) should be made in inverse ratio to the weights.

$$\frac{c_1}{1/w_1} = \frac{c_2}{1/w_2} = \frac{c_3}{1/w_3} = \frac{c_4}{1/w_4}, \text{ etc.} \quad \text{(where } c \text{ means "correction")}$$

But we have already seen that the weights vary inversely with the square of the standard error. Hence,

$$\frac{c_1}{(\sigma_m{}^2)_1} = \frac{c_2}{(\sigma_m{}^2)_2} = \frac{c_3}{(\sigma_m{}^2)_3} = \frac{c_4}{(\sigma_m{}^2)_4}, \text{ etc.}$$

or, stated another way, the adjustments ("corrections") vary *directly* as the square of the standard errors.

In the case of the triangle, of Art. 8–5, let us suppose the weights were as shown in the accompanying table. The computation would be:

Angle	Mean value	Weight (w)	Adjustment ratio	Adjust-ment*	Adjusted value
A	49° 46′ 45.7″	4	1/4 = 0.25	+00.4″	49° 46′ 46.1″
B	34° 51′ 39.8″	1	1/1 = 1.00	+01.5″	34° 51′ 41.3″
C	95° 21′ 31.8″	2	1/2 = 0.50	+00.8″	95° 21′ 32.6″
$\sum$	179° 59′ 57.3″			1.75 +02.7″	180° 00′ 00.0″

* Adjustment—(Total = 02.7″)   (Note that the adjustment is made in *inverse* ratio to the weights.)

for A: $\dfrac{0.25}{1.75} \times 02.7'' = 00.4''$

for B: $\dfrac{1.00}{1.75} \times 02.7'' = 01.5''$

for C: $\dfrac{0.50}{1.75} \times 02.7'' = 00.8''$

8–12 Unequal Weights, with Exact Check Value

As indicated earlier (Art. 8–5), the availability of an exact check value allows the adjustment of means of measurement sets so as to fit the exact condition, as the following examples illustrate.

EXAMPLE. A party did a differential level (tilting-type) run several times from bench mark 39 to bench mark 40, using careful techniques, and computed a mean result and σ_m. Later, using a less precise instrument and fewer runs, they ran back from 40 to 30 with a mean result and σ_m. Find the weighted mean of the values.

Set	Value (m)	σ_m	Weight ratio	Weight factor	vw
A	4.6123	± 0.0007	$(1/7)^2 = 2045$	2.96	8.88
B	4.6128	± 0.0012	$(1/12)^2 = 695$	1.00	8.00
Σ				3.96	16.88

$$\overline{M} = 4.6120 + \frac{16.88}{3.96} = 4.61243 \text{ meters}$$

Note the short cuts: (a) Weight ratios use only the significant figures. (b) In the last column, only the last digit of the number in the value column is multiplied by the weight factor. These keep the operations simple enough for slide-rule calculation. Analysis of significant figures will demonstrate the validity of such short-cutting.

EXAMPLE. At a given station a transit was used to measure four angles, closing the horizon. The value for each angle was found several times, and a σ_m for each angle was found, as shown in the table on the next page. Adjust the values by properly weighting them, as shown in Art. 8–11.

It will be noted that in each case of this adjustment, the *weights* were not used. Rather, the adjustment factors were obtained from the standard errors immediately. In other words, adjustments may be made in direct proportion to the square of the standard errors.

Angle	Value	σ_m	Adjustment ratio	Adjust-ment*	Adjusted values
AOB	34° 15′ 31″	±03″	$3^2 = 9$	−00.6″	34° 15′ 30.4″
BOC	23° 49′ 55″	±10″	$10^2 = 100$	−06.5″	23° 49′ 48.5″
COD	190° 50′ 54″	±05″	$5^2 = 25$	−01.6″	190° 50′ 52.4″
DOA	111° 03′ 49″	±02″	$2^2 = 4$	−00.3″	111° 03′ 48.7″
Σ	360° 00′ 09″		138	−09.0″	360° 00′ 00.0″

* Adjustment—(Total = 09.0″)

for *AOB*: $\dfrac{9}{138} \times 09 = 00.6''$

for *BOC*: $\dfrac{100}{138} \times 09 = 06.5''$, etc.

This is equivalent to adjusting the values in *inverse* ratio to their weights (and their weights vary *inversely* with the square of their standard errors).

PROBLEMS

1. In a pentagon the angles were measured as shown below (with the maximum error in each given).   Find the adjusted angles.

   (*a*) 107° 10′ 20.0″ ± 05.0″
   (*b*) 140   27   41.7 ± 02.5
   (*c*)   97   50   19.3 ± 02.5
   (*d*) 128   23   37.5 ± 05.0
   (*e*)   66   08   30.0 ± 10.0

2. Assuming that there is a further set of independent measurements of the complete length *AB* of Problem 3 of Chapter 7 giving 753.989 ± 0.012, find the weighted mean of the length *AB*.
3. The following data was taken on the dimensions of a triangular-shaped plot of ground.   What is the best value for the area?   What is the 90% error in each side's measurement?   Using the 90% errors, what will be the expected error of the area?

Measurement of Altitude	Measurement of Base
10.001	18.567
10.002	18.566
9.998	18.568
9.999	18.566
10.000	18.566
10.000	18.565
10.001	18.566
9.999	18.567
10.000	18.565
10.010	18.564

4. The developed horsepower in a direct-current motor may be expressed by the following relationship:

$$P_m = \frac{2\pi TN}{33,000}$$

where: P_m = mechanical power
$\quad\quad T$ = torque in lb-ft
$\quad\quad N$ = speed in revolutions per minute

What would be the "expected" power of a single motor and the standard deviation therefrom based on the following experimental data from the motors coming off the assembly line?

Measured torque (lb-ft)	Measured speed (rpm)
62.55	1,706
62.57	1,704
62.56	1,702
62.53	1,703
62.55	1,704
62.55	1,702
62.54	1,705
62.56	1,703
62.54	1,704
62.55	1,705
62.54	1,704
62.53	1,703
62.56	1,706
62.55	1,704
62.58	1,705

5. The following tabulation shows the results of observations made with a one-second theodolite. Each major group of 50 readings was recorded by a single observer, who used these procedures:

(a) The instrument was pointed at a well-defined target; the graduations were matched; and the reading (in seconds) was made, by estimation, to the nearest $\frac{1}{10}$ second.

(b) The micrometer wheel was turned to destroy the matching of the graduations, the graduations were then rematched, and a second reading was made. This operation was repeated to a total of 10 readings—the left column in each group of five.

(c) By turning the tangent screw, the instrument was thrown off the target, then repointed on the target, and another series of 10 micrometer readings was made.

(d) Each observer followed this routine for a total of five separate pointings on the target (about 100 ft away from the instrument) and 10 micrometer readings were made for each pointing.

Utilizing the "estimated mean" technique, work each column to find the mean of column, standard deviation, and standard error of the mean. For the five columns then find the weighted mean of all five columns.

Compare this result with the mean as determined by treating the 50 observations for each observer "en masse."

GROUP A

56.4	56.0	53.9	51.9	54.5
57.3	56.8	57.6	51.4	57.1
59.7	56.3	58.1	51.8	57.1
58.8	58.1	55.3	52.0	57.5
57.3	57.1	58.4	51.2	56.1
57.3	57.7	57.4	51.0	58.1
56.7	58.0	56.9	53.5	56.8
58.1	58.0	58.5	52.8	57.0
58.3	53.5	59.1	52.7	58.3
57.3	57.4	58.3	52.6	57.0

GROUP B

57.8	58.0	62.9	60.5	58.2
57.0	58.1	62.0	62.0	58.9
60.0	60.0	61.2	63.0	59.2
55.5	59.6	60.0	59.7	58.2
59.7	60.0	59.5	59.5	58.1
60.0	61.2	58.2	62.2	59.1

60.9	60.0	60.0	63.1	59.3
58.3	59.9	59.0	61.2	60.8
58.8	60.1	59.1	59.2	60.0
57.5	58.9	57.5	62.0	63.7

GROUP C

58.9	60.0	60.4	61.3	59.8
60.9	60.3	60.9	62.7	60.4
57.7	58.4	60.4	62.7	60.4
54.8	58.8	60.7	62.8	61.1
54.2	59.4	60.4	61.1	59.9
59.8	54.9	61.1	61.7	61.1
57.7	59.8	61.4	61.7	61.1
59.2	60.7	61.1	61.8	60.8
59.8	60.3	60.2	62.4	60.4
57.5	60.1	60.5	61.0	59.9

GROUP D

51.8	49.6	56.0	53.6	56.0
52.0	52.8	55.9	53.1	55.0
54.0	51.8	55.0	52.2	56.5
53.7	52.8	54.0	55.1	56.0
51.2	52.0	54.9	54.1	55.8
51.8	54.1	54.4	53.0	56.3
52.0	52.0	53.9	54.2	56.1
51.5	54.0	55.3	53.8	55.0
50.8	51.5	53.0	56.0	54.8
50.4	51.0	55.2	56.0	56.8

GROUP E

55.0	54.9	54.2	55.6	50.1
53.8	55.9	53.0	56.0	50.2
55.7	55.9	53.0	57.0	54.7
57.1	57.4	55.1	57.3	53.2
56.3	54.0	54.2	55.2	52.8
55.9	55.0	52.0	55.4	49.1
56.3	55.3	52.0	54.0	50.1
60.4	54.0	51.5	54.2	49.2
57.3	57.0	52.8	54.2	53.0
57.0	55.3	53.7	55.9	49.2

nine / *practical application of the theory of errors in measurement*

9–1   *Remarks*

In the preceding chapters we have discovered that to be absolutely sure and certain of a measurement we must repeat it nearly an infinite number of times (Chapter 3).   But since we do not have a thousand years to live, we must use a more economical method of making measurements.   It was subsequently indicated (Art. 6–2) that we can generally be fairly certain of our precision if we measure 10, 15, or 20 times.   But often enough we can still not afford even this smaller expenditure of effort.   Obviously, then, a more practical approach must be found.

9–2   *Standard Deviation a Criterion*

The clue to the solution of this number-of-measurements problem is seen in the analysis used to find the standard deviation itself. In Art. 3–7 it was noted that when measurements of a quantity are made in a given set, they must be all done under the same (standard) circumstances, by the same (standard) method if the results are to be comparable.   In a word, standard deviation (σ_s) applies only to identically made measurements.

With this in mind, it now becomes apparent that we must standardize on a measurement method which will give us a set of measurements that have a certain fixed standard error (σ_m) of a size that we can tolerate.   This, of course, would imply a method which will furnish a certain standard deviation (σ_s) for an individual measurement. The first step is to determine the acceptable maximum size of standard deviation.

9–3 *Fixing upon a Maximum Desired Error*

In the selection of the largest size of error that can be tolerated, we must view the measurement's place in the entire project. Its contribution to the computation must be examined to establish its influence on the final result.

Selecting too large a tolerable spread (too large a standard deviation) would possibly give too much leeway for sloppy work in making measurements, although it is frequently a desirable thing that a measurement be made only roughly. Such work would probably be characterized as "rough" or of "low-order precision" in this case, rather than "sloppy," because it would be essentially in keeping with the low precision demanded.

On the other hand, when a very tight spread is required, for very precise work, it will often be a very difficult and expensive procedure to meet this requirement. Here an economic balance must be struck in making demands for "first-quality" or "high-order" measurement.

9–4 *Selecting a "Maximum Error"*

Once the possible effect of the measured quantity is established, however, its tolerance can be fixed. The tolerance, limits of plus and minus error about a mean value, is effectively a precision of the measurements that are to be made. The tolerance says, in effect, that any single measured quantity must lie between certain values. If we wish to fix this at a maximum allowable error, it will mean that the limits of "maximum" error $(3.29\sigma_s)$ can be set so we have 100% certainty of our measurement. (See Summary Table, Art. 5–13.)

It is possible, though, that a less rigid "maximum" or acceptable error might be used, say, $3\sigma_s$ or $2\sigma_s$ or the "90% error" $(1.64\sigma_s)$. This will frequently make for considerably less effort, though at a risk that some 1% or 5% or 10% of the measurements will have greater errors than the prescribed maximum. Here again we must balance this risk against the economics of the given situation. Many times it will be entirely admissible to use a lesser degree of certainty, especially if additional precautions (check measurements by another procedure, for example) are employed.

9–5 *Procedure for Limiting the Error*

Let us re-examine the limits of error we should consider satis-factory, and ascertain therefrom a method of achieving the security of knowing that our measurements will not exceed such an arbitrarily fixed limiting error.   Suppose, for example, we wish to measure an angle and be certain it is not more than $\pm 05''$ from the "truth." We could go through our infinite-number-of-measurements routine, or we could simply use a routine for measurement that is known to produce this size of standard deviation (σ_s), or this size of "maxi-mum" error ($3.29\sigma_s$), or this size of 90% error ($1.64\sigma_s$), etc.   If such a fixed routine (e.g., using a 10-second repeating theodolite and measuring twice or four times) has already been established, we can utilize this routine and then reasonably believe our result will be within the limits desired.

9–6 *Standardizing the Procedure*

After having fixed the precision to be demanded in the measure-ment, we must examine procedural methods and fix upon one which will give the desired result.   If the measurement (or one similar to it) has never before been made, it will be necessary to make very many measurements of the same kind to establish the validity of the procedure and to enable a study of the precision obtainable.   Such a case occurred when the speed of light was ascertained by use of a "measured mile" some years ago.

The ingredients of the method must be scrutinized for elimination of all but random errors, and then the results must be analyzed for scatter, standard deviation, etc., to discover the precision which can be expected from the method employed.   Then the procedure can be fairly well characterized as being precise to $\pm \sigma_s$ (68.3% of the time) or $\pm 2\sigma_s$ (95% of the time), etc.

9–7 *Utilizing a Standard Procedure*

Once the precision of the method or procedure is fixed by an "infinity" of measurements, however, and once the details of procedure are spelled out, it is apparent that, when the method is used and all of its prescribed details are adhered to, the results will be similar.   In other words, a careful execution of a standard procedure enables us to rely on a whole family of measurements made by this procedure.   We thus utilize the results of many hundreds of measurements made similarly at other times and other places, other quantities by other people, to warrant or guarantee the precision (and hence the accuracy) of our present measurement.

Consequently, reliance is placed upon procedures. This is why procedures are spelled out so meticulously in specifications, why there is exchange of procedural information, and why we are always anxious to learn about how the other fellow did it and what results he got. This utilization of established standard procedures and instruments is the clue to making reliable measurements, and is one of the most important outcomes of all the considerations thus far.

A typical summary sheet of specifications for triangulation, traverse, and leveling is given in Appendix D. These are the standard U.S. Coast and Geodetic Survey specifications for measurement, and contain built-in checks and safeguards resulting from years of use. Familiar laboratory manuals of many varieties will give measurement procedures, testing methods, etc., to establish for the user an assurance of precision (thus accuracy) if only a very few measurements or tests are to be made. Having followed established procedures, then, we are justifiably permitted to "adopt" as our own an established value of standard deviation for a single measurement.

EXAMPLE. It has been established that, by following "first-order" specifications, a level party can attain a difference of elevation within ± 0.017 ft $\sqrt{M}$, and by following "second-order" specifications, within ± 0.035 ft $\sqrt{M}$, where M is miles. Party A did 6 miles of first-order leveling from bench mark P to bench mark Q; party B, going from P to Q by another route, did 4 miles of second-order level work. Assuming that these formulae give limiting or maximum error, assign weights and adjust the elevation of bench mark Q, given the elevation of $P = 1,471.612$ ft.

Party	Difference of elevation (feet)	Order of work	Miles	Limiting error	Square of error	Adjustment factor	Adjustment	Adjusted values
A	49.018	1st	6	$\pm 0.017\sqrt{6}$	0.0018	1*	$+0.0124$	49.0304
B	49.064	2nd	4	$\pm 0.035\sqrt{4}$	0.0049	2.72	-0.0336	49.0304
	0.046			* $\frac{1}{3.72}$ 0.046		3.72	0.0460	

This example shows a lower-order measurement influencing one of higher order, something not often permitted in practice (for reasons extraneous to the present discussion). There is no reason to prohibit such a happening, provided the adjustment to each of the values lies within the range accepted as maximum or limiting error for each value. In this example these are:

Measurement	Accepted limiting error	Adjustment
First-order	$\pm 0.017\sqrt{6} = \pm 0.042$	$+0.0124$
Second-order	$\pm 0.035\sqrt{4} = \pm 0.070$	-0.0336

Adjustments of such magnitude as to exceed the range would be out of order: in such a case some blunder or undiscovered systematic error should be suspected in either or both sets of measurements.

The higher-order result (49.018) is known to be other than the true value, and it is a valid presumption that the lower-order result (49.064) can give some indication as to where the true value lies with respect to the reported first-order value. The adjustment procedure is consequently that of Art. 8–10.

The point to be made is that each of the measurement results has the validity bestowed upon it by virtue of the established procedures used to obtain it. Therefore, each value can legitimately bestow its influence upon the final result and validly contribute its weight in finding the adjusted mean.

The actual elevation of Q can be found from the known elevation of P by adding or subtracting the 49.030 ft. Notice that unless we can rely on established procedure for confidence in our precision, we are forced to perform great amounts of repetitious measurement.

Here is another example, illustrating the reliance that can be placed upon a pattern of previously established results, the performance records of two measurement devices (or systems).

EXAMPLE. In a measurement of a distance RS by two different electronic distance-measuring devices, each with its well-established accuracy, a weighted mean can be ascertained from a set of measurements made by each. Instrument A: Accuracy of 1 part in 300,000 of the length ± 2 in.; length reported as 3,516.71 ft. Instrument B:

Model 4D Geodimeter has a range of 2 to 3 miles in daylight and 15 to 20 miles at night.   A modulated light beam is projected from the instrument to a glass prism reflector placed over the unknown point.   The light is returned to the instrument and the distance is determined utilizing a phase comparison technique.   The instrument is highly accurate and has built-in safety features, eliminating possible operator's errors as well as computation errors.   The average length of line measured with Geodimeter equipment is $\frac{1}{2}$ to 1 mile. The average error is only in the order of 1 cm ($\frac{3}{8}$ in.) $\pm$ 2 millionths of the distance.

Practical Application of the Theory of Errors in Measurement / 75

Accuracy of 5 parts in 1,000,000 of the length ±0.04 ft; length as 3,516.49 ft.

The establishment accuracies of each instrument can be used as the standard error of each value shown. Each value is in reality the mean of a set of four or six measurements. The individual errors are combined as follows:

$$\text{Instrument } A: \quad \sigma_m = \pm \sqrt{\left(\frac{3517 \times 1}{3 \times 10^5}\right)^2 + \left(\frac{2}{12}\right)^2}$$

$$= \pm \sqrt{0.000138 + 0.0278} = \pm \sqrt{0.0279}$$

$$= \pm 0.167 \text{ ft}$$

$$\text{Instrument } B: \quad \sigma_m = \pm \sqrt{\left(\frac{3517 \times 5}{10^6}\right)^2 + (0.04)^2}$$

$$= \pm \sqrt{0.000309 + 0.0016} = \pm \sqrt{0.0019}$$

$$= \pm 0.044 \text{ ft}$$

Instru- ment	Value (less 3516.00)	σ_m	Weight ratio	Weight factor	vw
A	0.71	±0.167	$\left(\frac{1}{0.167}\right)^2 = 36$	1	0.71
B	0.49	±0.044	$\left(\frac{1}{0.044}\right)^2 = 517$	14.4	7.05
				15.4	7.76

$$\overline{M} = 3516.00 + \frac{7.76}{15.4} = 3516.50 \text{ ft}$$

We may reasonably accept this $\overline{M}$ value because both electronic instruments have been tested and used for many years according to the fixed pattern of procedure here employed, and because their results have been checked over and over against lengths that have been established firmly by other methods.

9-8 *Setting Specifications for a Standard Procedure*

Setting up a procedure for making measurements can be a tedious task, because a complete analysis must be made of the entire operation to determine the degree of leeway that can be accorded each step. Though we speak of analyzing from the desired precision back through to the actual procedure, the usual (and the simpler) way is to analyze forward, using the cut-and-try approach. A trial procedure is established and the analysis of errors is carried through to establish the overall precision to be expected. If the precision is satisfactory, the procedure can be pronounced good; if too low, then certain steps in the procedure must be tightened up; and, if too high, certain steps may be relaxed. Out of such cut-and-try analysis will evolve a standard measuring procedure. Frequently, many attempts must be made before evolving a satisfactory measurement procedure that provides the desired precision of result.

In Appendix C there are some extended analyses of procedures in measurement developed as indicated herein. By following through those shown, a clearer understanding of this treatment can be achieved.

PROBLEMS

1. Write a specification for laying out a 1,000-meter distance for an Olympic race that must be accurate to ± 0.2 meter. Assume that there is a 50-meter tape available and that it is correct to ± 0.0005 meter under the prevailing temperature, tension, and other handling conditions. Merely ascertain what precision must be used in marking the tape-lengths.

2. Calculate the illustrative problem of Appendix C (as suggested in step 4) until a precision of 1:10,000 is obtained. (*Hint:* Note what change will occur in the e^2 column for any individual change.) Write the specifications.

3. Calculate the illustrative problem of Appendix C by using the E_t as cumulative (as suggested in step 2b.) Write the specifications.

4. Calculate the illustrative problem of Appendix C by holding the tape on the ground (assume smooth pavement, for instance.) Assume that a hand level is used to measure the slope between tape ends to ± 1 ft. (*Hint:* Will e_g then be cumulative? What becomes of e_s? How rewrite the specification for marking?)

5. Calculate the problem by using a 50-ft steel tape.

6. Several elevation determinations were made on a questionable foundation at La Guardia Airport during the autumn and several more during the spring, always working from a firm bench mark 0.8 mile away. From the data, calculate the elevation in the fall, with its various sigma errors, and again in the spring to see if there has been definite settlement. (Assume that the "closure" values of

Appendix D are in this case equivalently the 2-sigma error of each level run.)

Autumn			Spring		
Run no.	Elevation	Order	Run no.	Elevation	Order
1	8.2462	3rd	7	8.2479	2nd
2	8.2478	1st	8	8.2452	3rd
3	8.2467	2nd	9	8.2467	1st
4	8.2481	1st	10	8.2473	2nd
5	8.2480	1st	11	8.2479	1st
6	8.2469	2nd	12	8.2475	2nd

ten / two-dimensional errors

10–1 *General*

The previous work with normal distribution of random errors deals with only one-dimensional (linear) error theory. Measurements of lengths, elevations, angles, and such items have one-dimensional errors which can be handled by such theory. The principles of error theory can then be used advantageously to analyze the results and to fix the specifications for a survey or other measuring procedure.

However, when it becomes needful to examine the accuracy of a position in a plane with respect to two axes, a further error analysis must be employed. The linear error component of two- and three-dimensional positions can be analyzed by applying the principles of normal linear error distribution. Two-dimensional error analysis will be the subject of the ensuing articles.

10–2 *Definition*

A two-dimensional error affecting a quantity is one defined by two random variables. For instance, the location of a point B set on the ground intended to be N 5,200.000 and E 1,400.000 is affected by two variables, direction and distance (or possibly by two distances only). In the (exaggerated) sketch of Fig. 12 it becomes apparent.

Since error exists (either $+$ or $-$) in the measured length of AB and in the measured direction of AB, then the rectangle 1, 2, 3, 4 would seem to define the location of the possibly true position of B. Conversely, if we assume that B as plotted is the true or correct position of B, the rectangle may be regarded as the limit for the positioning of B when it is laid out.

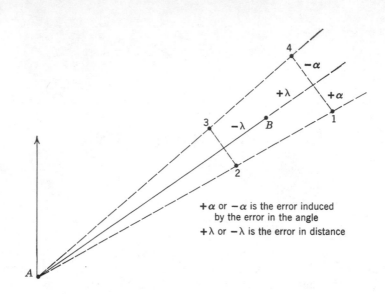

FIGURE 12

10–3 *The Probability Ellipse*

If we consider that $\pm\lambda$ is the error in the distance and $\pm\alpha$ the error resulting from direction error, assuming each is random and independent, then the probability (linear) density distribution of each error is:

$$p_\lambda = \frac{1}{\sigma_\lambda \sqrt{2h}}\, e^{-\lambda^2/2\sigma_\lambda^2}$$

$$p_\alpha = \frac{1}{\sigma_\alpha \sqrt{2h}}\, e^{-\alpha^2/2\sigma_\alpha^2}$$

The probability of each occurring simultaneously is $(p_\lambda)(p_\alpha)$, giving a two-dimensional probability density distribution:

$$(p_\lambda)(p_\alpha) = \frac{1}{(\sigma_\lambda)(\sigma_\alpha)2h}\, e^{-\left(\frac{\lambda^2}{2\sigma_\lambda^2} + \frac{\alpha^2}{2\sigma_\alpha^2}\right)}$$

This can be written as:

$$(p_\lambda)(p_\alpha)\sigma_\lambda\sigma_\alpha 2h = e^{-\frac{1}{2}\left(\frac{\lambda^2}{\sigma_\lambda^2} + \frac{\alpha^2}{\sigma_\alpha^2}\right)}$$

80 / Engineering Measurements

Therefore,

$$-2 \ln (p_\lambda p_\alpha \sigma_\lambda \sigma_\alpha 2h) = \frac{\lambda^2}{\sigma_\lambda{}^2} + \frac{\alpha^2}{\sigma_\alpha{}^2}$$

Since, for given values of p_λ and p_α, the left-hand member is a constant, then:

$$K^2 = \frac{\lambda^2}{\sigma_\lambda{}^2} + \frac{\alpha^2}{\sigma_\alpha{}^2}$$

This shows that, for values of $(p_\lambda)(p_\alpha)$ varying from 0 to ∞, a family of equal probability density ellipses will occur with axes $k\sigma_\lambda$ and $k\sigma_\alpha$.

10–4 *The Probability Circle*

But, if $\sigma_\lambda = \sigma_\alpha$, the equation can be seen to be that of a circle (really an equal-axis ellipse), since by substituting and rearranging terms, we obtain:

$$-2\sigma_\lambda{}^2 \ln [p_\lambda p_\alpha \sigma_\lambda{}^2 (2h)] = \lambda^2 + \alpha^2$$

If we note that the left-hand member of the equation is a constant, say, $(k_1 r)^2$, the circular form becomes apparent:

$$(k_1 r)^2 = \lambda^2 + \alpha^2$$

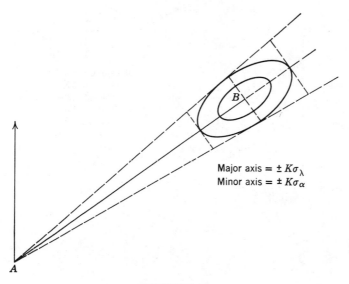

Major axis = $\pm K\sigma_\lambda$
Minor axis = $\pm K\sigma_\alpha$

FIGURE 13

Two-Dimensional Errors | 81

Thus far we have been working with an error in length λ and an error in direction α. It now becomes apparent that, if we utilize measurement methods to keep λ approximately equal to α, the resulting error ellipse becomes approximately an error circle. We may then expect that our errors with respect to our coordinate axes will have exactly the same values, meaning that:

$$\sigma_\lambda = \sigma_\alpha = \sigma_x = \sigma_y$$

(See Fig. 14.)

We may then conclude that the error circle will have a radius

$$k_2 = \sqrt{E_x{}^2 + E_y{}^2}$$

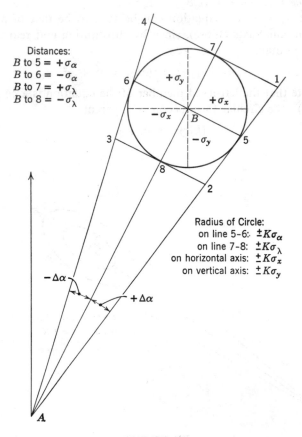

Distances:
B to 5 = $+\sigma_\alpha$
B to 6 = $-\sigma_\alpha$
B to 7 = $+\sigma_\lambda$
B to 8 = $-\sigma_\lambda$

Radius of Circle:
on line 5-6: $\pm K\sigma_\alpha$
on line 7-8: $\pm K\sigma_\lambda$
on horizontal axis: $\pm K\sigma_x$
on vertical axis: $\pm K\sigma_y$

FIGURE 14

where E_x and E_y are any values of coordinate error. For convenience, let us call the errors in the X and Y coordinates respectively x and y. We see then that the previous elliptical probability density equation can be properly written:

$$p_x p_y \sigma_x \sigma_y (2h) = e^{-\frac{1}{2}\left(\frac{x^2}{\sigma_x^2} + \frac{y^2}{\sigma_y^2}\right)}$$

By analogous reasoning, we arrive at the probability density circle:

$$(Kr)^2 = x^2 + y^2$$

10–5 Elliptical (Circular) Error Evaluation

The probability density function when integrated gives the probability distribution function (the s curve). The probability of an ellipse is given by the distribution function:

$$P_{(x,y)} = 1 - e^{-K^2/2}$$

Solving this equation for various values of K yields these values for probability percentages in the accompanying table.

Probability (P)	K
39.4%	1.000
50.0%	1.177
63.2%	1.414
90.0%	2.146
99.0%	3.035
99.8%	3.500

The meaning is that when $K =$ unity, for instance, 39.4% of all errors in a circular distribution will be within the limits of the circular standard deviation σ_c. This means, for example, that when $K = 1.0000$, the axes of the ellipse are $1.0000\sigma_x$ and $1.0000\sigma_y$ (giving a circle of radius $\sigma_x = \sigma_y$) and that there is a 39.4% probability that the actual position errors in x and y will fall simultaneously within that circle. Increasing the diameter of the circle to $3.5000\sigma_c$ ($= 3.5000\sigma_z = 3.5000\sigma_y$) will give a 99.8% probability that both the x and the y error will fall within the circle.

Therefore, in the simple case of measuring to set out a point Q from point P, we must keep the length error consistent with the error resulting from direction.

EXAMPLE. To set point Q with a maximum error of ± 0.05 ft, what shall be the limiting errors tolerated in distance and direction?

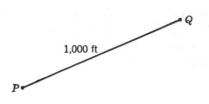

1,000 ft

Strictly,

$$0.05 \text{ ft} = r = \sqrt{E_z^2 + E_y^2} = \sqrt{E_L^2 + E_a^2}$$

(a) Since

$$E_L = E_a, \qquad 0.05 = \sqrt{2E_L^2} = E_L\sqrt{2}$$

and

$$E_L = \pm 0.035 \text{ ft}$$

This demands, therefore, a measurement precision ratio of $\pm 0.035/1000 = 1/28{,}000$. Reference to Specifications (Appendix D) shows that this is a traverse of between first and second order.

(b) The angle (directional) error may not exceed

$E_a = 0.035 \text{ ft} = 1000 \sin \varDelta\alpha$ $\qquad$ and $\qquad$ $\varDelta\alpha = \sin^{-1} 0.000035$

Since $\tan 01' = \sin 01' = 0.00029$, and since small angles vary as their sines,

$$\varDelta\alpha = \frac{0.000035}{0.00029} = 0.121' = \pm 07.3'' \text{ of arc}$$

Note that this angular error limitation assumes a single sighting 1,000 ft long. Practical difficulties frequently render such a long sighting difficult or impracticable.

EXAMPLE. In the preceding example, if three instrument set-ups have to be made, to bring the final direction error to less than

± 0.035, more careful work must be done. Let $E_a = \pm 0.035$ ft as before, but let each sighting now be 333 ft. This means effectively that the first sighting has an error in angle $\Delta\alpha$ that casts its effect 1,000 ft, the second also a $\Delta\alpha$ that casts its effect 666 ft, and the third a $\Delta\alpha$ that casts its effect 333 ft. Effectively at point B these displacement errors are, respectively, as shown in the accompanying table.

	E	E^2
1	$\pm 1,000 \sin \Delta\alpha$	$1,000,000 \sin^2 \Delta\alpha$
2	$\pm 666 \sin \Delta\alpha$	$440,000 \sin^2 \Delta\alpha$
3	$\pm 333 \sin \Delta\alpha$	$110,000 \sin^2 \Delta\alpha$
Σ		$1,550,000 \sin^2 \Delta\alpha$

Since

$$E_a = \pm \sqrt{E_1^2 + E_2^2 + E_3^2}$$

$$\pm 0.035 \text{ ft} = \sqrt{1,550,000 \sin^2 \Delta\alpha} = 1,242 \sin \Delta\alpha$$

$$\sin \Delta\alpha = 0.000028$$

$$\Delta\alpha = \frac{0.000028}{0.00029} = \pm 0.0965' = \pm 05.8''$$

This means that if we wish to keep the resulting position error within the known circular limits, we must use consistent distance and direction procedures. If in (a) we wish to keep the position of point Q of our example 99.8% assuredly within a circle of 0.05 ft radius, we must therefore acknowledge that the E_L and E_a (really the E_x and E_y also) are $3.5000\sigma_x$ and $3.5000\sigma_y$. Consequently our measurements must be made (in the example) to $\pm 0.035/3.500 = \pm 0.010$ ft. Otherwise, as the example now stands, there will be only a 39.4% assurance.

10–6 *Application to Position Accuracy*
Now what does all this mean in the context of position accuracy? Must we always compute position error for individual points in

question? Can the accuracy of these points be known? Or can we devise a means of stating position accuracy in a general way for all points in a system, be they set or located by traverse, triangulation, direct measurement, trilateration, or some other method.

To achieve consistency between distance precision and angular precision, we may simply note that this equality should obtain:

$$\frac{\sigma_\lambda}{\text{Distance}} = \sigma_\alpha$$

The relative error in distance should equal the angular error in radians. The typical values in the accompanying table derive therefrom:

Precision in direction	Precision in distance
1°	1:57
10′	1:344
05′	1:690
01′	1:3440
30″	1:6870
20″	1:10,310
10″	1:20,620
01″	1:206,200

In the case of the preceding example, line PQ was used to set Point Q, though no mention was made of the positional accuracy of point P. If we knew, for instance, that point P had a positional accuracy of ± 0.05 ft in X and in Y, this error would have to be reckoned with in setting point Q. The $(E_z)_P$ and the $(E_z)_{PQ}$ must be summed thus to get $(E_z)_Q$:

$$\sqrt{(E_z)_P{}^2 + (E_z)_{PQ}{}^2} = (E_z)_Q$$

Of course, this cannot be done for each line. Instead, a procedure is worked up for distance measurement and angle (direction) measurement which will constitute a system that gives the desired accuracy. It is checked extensively to assure that the summation of all accidental errors will not exceed a certain desired maximum value for 50% (or 90% or 99.8%) of the time. Specifications are spelled out in careful instructions, and this then becomes the assurance of the resulting positional accuracy. Such a set of summary specifications is given in Appendix D for traversing and for triangulation. Working within the limits there prescribed can be expected to assure the desired positional accuracy.

10–7   Use of Control Systems

At this point it may be advisable to read the special section in Appendix E on the geoid, since it may be of assistance in understanding the present reasoning.

Essentially the question of positioning points on the surface of the earth (on the geoid, or on the ellipsoid adopted as its mathematical expression) is primarily a matter of using properly spaced and adequate control points. By some higher-order method such as astronomical observations, coupled with careful linking of observation stations by measurements between them, a control network can be established. The positional accuracy of these control stations can be computed from analysis of the errors of the astronomical and ground measurement methods. Then measurements and surveys of smaller areas can be linked to the larger well-controlled network, much as the skeleton of the body is the framework onto which and into which various bodily organs fit.

The use of such a control network thus precludes the errors that would tend to accumulate if the survey were to be extended piece by piece from one point outward without external check points. Whenever such a small survey is used and is extended from one starting point, at appropriate and available control stations of the network a comparison of X and Y positions can be made. Adjustments can be made to the better-fixed values of X and Y coordinates by common-sense methods, and the strength of the higher-order control network is thus utilized and extended throughout the minor system.

This notion of over-all control is as essential to small operations as it is to nationwide or worldwide surveying and mapping. Carpenters and bricklayers set the corners of a building and work from these controlling points; a ship, an airplane, an automobile, or a large machine is similarly put together from controlling axes and points, not by the accretion method. The setting of this type of control for production operations is frequently done today by using the optical tooling procedure which essentially utilizes the equipment and methods of surveying.

PROBLEMS

1. A lighted target 10,000 ft distant is observed with a theodolite to within one-tenth second of angle (by use of a repetition technique). The distance to the point is measured by a radar-frequency distance-measuring device to within 0.012 ft. Is there consistency between angular and distance techniques? If not, ascertain what should be the proper angular error value.

2. If point B in the preceding problem is located with a 50% assurance within a circle of 0.01 ft radius, what is the radius of the circle for 90% assurance?

3. With present technology it is feasible to measure from Florida to California (approximately 3,000 miles) and be 50% sure of distance within ±140 ft. If a theodolite were used to measure the angles between adjoining segments of this line (assuming 300 angles), what angular error would be the maximum permissible?

4. Assuming that a rangefinder can give distance of 3,000 ft within a 90% accuracy of ±200 ft, what angular accuracy would be sufficient? What if the distance accuracy were ±100 ft? What if 10 ft?

Appendices

appendix A / significant figures in measurement

A-1   *Exact versus Doubtful Figures*

When a measurement is made, all digits in the result are *exact* if
they are obtained by counting or by noting that a point lies between
two markers, but digits are *doubtful* when they result from estimating.
On a ruler graduated only in full inches, the digits 11 are exact;
but if the height of a book can be measured as 11.2 in., the estimated
2 is doubtful or uncertain.   However, all three figures are significant.
Significant figures include all exact digits and one doubtful digit.
(It would be wrong and misleading in this case to call the book
11.21 in. or 11.213 in. high, since the smallest division on the ruler
is 1 in. and the eye can at best estimate to only tenths.   In this
instance, too, we may say merely that it is 11.2 in., but certainly not
11.20 in. or 11.200 in.   Why?)

A-2   *Use of Significant Figures*

In general, only those figures or digits which are the result of
actual measurement or calculation from an actual measurement are
said to be significant.   (Values which result from counting are, of
course, exact and are not here subject to discussion.)   Rules and
conventions, based on common sense, are detailed here.

A-3   *Use of Zero*

A. The zero is not significant when it serves merely to place the
decimal:

(1) 0.00275 meter contains three significant figures; this would
be clearer, perhaps, if written 2.75×10^{-3} meter.

(2) 54,000 miles has two significant figures (unless the intent is clearly that the value is exact). The use of the form 5.4 × 10^4 or 54 × 10^3 is not common, but it would be better usage in this respect.

B. When the zero is used otherwise, it is significant:
   (1) 5.7008 or 6.7760 or 6,500.0 each has five significant figures;
   (2) 0.0077650 also has five significant figures, and it could well be written 77.650 × 10^{-4} for clarity.

A–4 *Rules of Thumb for Significant Figures*
   A. Unless some precision index, such as sigma-value or standard error, is affixed, as

$$a = 1.755 \pm 0.003$$

the usual interpretation for the last (doubtful) figure is plus or minus one-half of a unit in the last column. Thus a measured length of, say, 26.817 ft means that the range of uncertainty extends from 26.8165 to 26.8175 ft.

   B. While we expect and use only one doubtful figure in the final result, it is desirable to use two uncertain figures throughout the calculation and round off at the end.

   C. Adding and subtracting: The sum or difference of several values is to be watched for doubtful figures. Note these obvious examples:

4.71	2.03	178.612
3.0	10.066	2.1
2.008	8.0412	176.5
9.7	20.14	

   D. Multiplying or dividing: The result must not be credited with more significant digits than appear in the term with the fewest number of significant figures:

   4.9178 × 2.03 = 9.98   (not 9.983134)
   $(67.81 × 10^3)^2$ = 4,598 × 10^6 (not 4,598.1961 × 10^6)
   456.212 ÷ 2.17 = 210   (not 210.2359447)

Note, however, that 8 and 9 are nearly 2-digit numbers, and occasionally an extra significant digit is thus warranted:
   9.612 × 3.00251 = 28.860   (but not 28.86012612)

E. The 10-in. slide rule is capable of just better than 3 digits.

F. In using logarithms, the number of decimal places required in the mantissa is fixed by the number of significant figures in the numbers being multiplied. Thus a six-place table is required for:

$$326.712 \times 41.6123$$

A–5 *Rounding Off*

When dropping excess digits, raise the last one to remain if the discarded quantity is greater than $\frac{1}{2}$, or leave it unchanged if the discarded quantity is less than $\frac{1}{2}$, thus

$$3.476 \quad \text{becomes} \quad 3.48 \quad \text{or} \quad 3.5$$
$$3.512 \quad \text{becomes} \quad 3.51 \quad \text{or} \quad 3.5$$

If the quantity to be discarded is just 5, then round off the preceding digit to the nearest *even* value, thus:

$$4.875 \quad \text{becomes} \quad 4.88 \quad \text{(or 4.9)}$$
$$4.885 \quad \text{becomes} \quad 4.88 \quad \text{(or 4.9)}$$
$$4.8749 \quad \text{becomes} \quad 4.87 \quad \text{(or 4.9)}$$
$$4.8851 \quad \text{becomes} \quad 4.89 \quad \text{(or 4.9)}$$

appendix B / basic concepts of probability and the normal probability curve

Linked to the notion of chance is the notion of probability (likelihood) of an occurrence such as the 50–50 chance of a tossed coin's coming up "heads." We can calculate such probabilities of events that are likely to occur, just as we can check the actuality of occurrences in controlled experimentation. Probability can be defined as the ratio of frequency of occurrence to the number of possible occurrences, i.e., number of successes to number of trials.

The probability of an event (e.g., three coins coming up heads) lies between 0% and 100% (or between 0 and 1). With one die, the probability of rolling a number between 1 and 6 inclusive is 100% (or 1). The probability of rolling the number 5 is 1/6 or 16.7%; the probability of its not being 5 is 100% − 16.7% = 83.3%.

The probability of *either* of two happenings (e.g., rolling a 5 or a 6) is the sum of their individual probabilities; in this case, 1/6 + 1/6 = 1/3 or 33.3%.

The probability of two events occurring simultaneously (e.g., rolling a 5 and then a 6) is the product of the individual probabilities, in this case (1/6)(1/6) = 1/36 or 2.8%. Note that the probability of rolling a 5 and a 6 with two dice, however, is (2/6)(1/6) = 1/18 = 5.56%.

The following table illustrates the probability concept, utilizing two dice rolled simultaneously. As shown in Fig. B1 on page 95, plotting these probabilities in a bar graph, called a histogram, will represent visually the probability of rolling any given number.

No.	All possible combinations	Probability	%
1	None	$(0/6)(6/6) = 0/36$	0.00
2	(1, 1)	$(1/6)(1/6) = 1/36$	2.78
3	(1, 2), (2, 1)	$(2/6)(1/6) = 2/36$	5.56
4	(1, 3), (2, 2), (3, 1)	$(3/6)(1/6) = 3/36$	8.33
5	(1, 4), (2, 3), (3, 2), (4, 1)	$(4/6)(1/6) = 4/36$	11.11
6	(1, 5), (2, 4), (3, 3), (4, 2), (5, 1)	$(5/6)(1/6) = 5/36$	13.89
7	(1, 6), (2, 5), (3, 4), (4, 3), (5, 2), (6, 1)	$(6/6)(1/6) = 6/36$	16.67
8	(2, 6), (3, 5), (4, 4), (5, 3), (6, 2)	$(5/6)(1/6) = 5/36$	13.89
9	(3, 6), (4, 5), (5, 4), (6, 3)	$(4/6)(1/6) = 4/36$	11.11
10	(4, 6), (5, 5), (6, 4)	$(3/6)(1/6) = 3/36$	8.33
11	(5, 6), (6, 5)	$(2/6)(1/6) = 2/36$	5.56
12	(6, 6)	$(1/6)(1/6) = 1/36$	2.78
13	None	$(0/6)(6/6) = 0/36$	0.00
		$\Sigma = 36/36$	100.00

A smooth curve is superimposed to represent the limits of possibility, thus giving the *area* beneath the curve the probability value of 1.0 or 100%, as the column summations indicate. The probability of rolling a 9 or 10 or 11 is the *sum* of their respective probabilities (see columnar tally in table): 9/36 or 25%. This is the area beneath the curve which corresponds to the number 9 to 11 inclusive, 9/36 or 25%. (Note that each box of Fig. B1 represents an area of 1/36, and there are 36/36 = 1.0 or 100% certainty of rolling a number from 2 to 12 inclusive.)

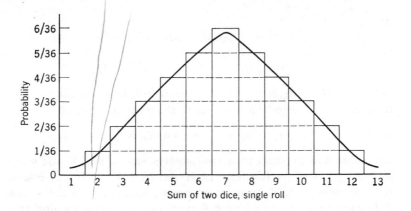

FIGURE B1 Histogram showing probability of rolling any given number with a single roll of two dice (with the probability density curve plotted).

If the number of dice thrown in a single roll were greater (say, about 10), the smooth curve would approach the bell-shaped "normal probability curve." Any segment of the area, then, beneath the probability curve is seen to represent the probability of an occurrence within the boundaries of the area.

DERIVATION OF NORMAL PROBABILITY CURVE

Let us suppose that we are recording a particular item (or parameter) of data, M, and that n readings of this parameter are taken. If each of these readings were taken with equal care, and a sufficient number of readings were taken, it can be said that the true value, as nearly as can be ascertained, or the most probable value of the parameter M will be the arithmetic mean, that is,

$$\overline{M} = \frac{\sum M_n}{n}$$

By working with the above equation we find that the number of readings multiplied by the arithmetic mean must be equal to the sum of the individual readings, that is,

$$n\overline{M} = \sum M_n$$

or

$$\overline{M} + \overline{M} + \overline{M} + \cdots + \overline{M} = M_1 + M_2 + \cdots + M_n$$

or

$$(\overline{M} - M_1) + (\overline{M} - M_2) + \cdots + (\overline{M} - M_n) = 0$$

but since $\overline{M} - M_n$ is the error of each individual reading and is denoted by x_n, we see that the sum of the errors is zero, or

$$x_1 + x_2 + x_3 + \cdots + x_n = 0$$

If we were now to consider two parameters, say, M and N, and make n observations of the functions of M and N, it would be possible to find the most probable value or arithmetic mean of M and N. The difference between particular observations and corresponding true values of the functions are the errors, each of which is a function of the parameters M and N. That is, errors are functions of the true value of a parameter. For example, there would be a larger absolute error in measuring a mile than in measuring a foot, generally speaking.

Now we can say that the probability of an error would be a function of the error. That is, if we denote probability by p, we have:

$$p_1 = f(x_1)$$
$$p_2 = f(x_2)$$
$$p_3 = f(x_n)$$

When we say that the probability of an error is a function of the error we mean that small errors are very probable and large errors are very improbable. A simple example will illustrate this. If we were measuring a distance of the order of 8 ft, an error of a foot would be highly improbable, whereas an error of an inch would be probable. Hence, the probability of an error is a function of the magnitude of the error and this, in turn, is somewhat a function of the true value.

With a little thought it is easily ascertained that the probability of committing the given system of errors, that is, making all the possible errors simultaneously, would be

$$P = (p_1)(p_2)(p_3) \ldots (p_n)$$

Therefore,

$$p = f(x_1) \cdot f(x_2) \cdot f(x_3) \cdot \cdots \cdot f(x_n)$$

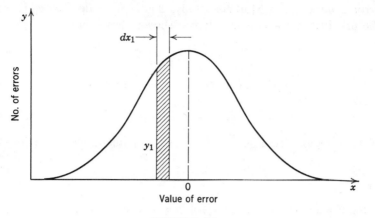

FIGURE B2

This means that since the absolute true value can never be ascertained by direct measurement, any measurement taken will have some error, even though it is small, and hence we will always commit an error. Therefore, let us designate the probability of the whole system of errors as 1, or 100%.

If we plot the number of occurrences of each error against the particular value of the error, we get a curve something like Fig. B2—assuming a usual occurrence pattern or distribution. If we examine the curve in Fig. B2, we see that the probability of committing an error dx_1 is equal to the shaded area under the curve, i.e., the area $y_1 \, dx_1$. Thus,

$$p_1 = y_1 \, dx_1$$

The probability density function integrated from $-\infty$ to $+\infty$ will yield 1 (or 100%). This is equivalent to stating that the area under the plotted curve contains 100% of all the errors.

It is obvious that if we let dx approach zero, the probability of the error will be proportional to the ordinate y. That is,

$$p_1 = ky_1$$

Let us now seek to design the equation of the normal probability curve in Fig. B2. If we are interested in determining the most probable value of an error, we are actually interested in rendering the

Basic Concepts of Probability / 97

error a minimum. Mathematically, this is equivalent to equating the first derivative to zero. It was shown above that:

$$P = p_1 \cdot p_2 \cdot p_3 \cdot \cdots \cdot p_n \tag{1a}$$

or

$$P = f(x_1) \cdot f(x_2) \cdot f(x_3) \cdot \cdots \cdot f(x_n) \tag{1b}$$

Now

$$f(x_1) = y\,dx = p$$

If we disregard the differential dx for the moment, we can write

$$y = f(x_1) \cdot f(x_2) \cdot f(x_3) \cdot \cdots \cdot f(x_n) \tag{1c}$$

or

$$\log y = \log f(x_1) + \log f(x_2) + \log f(x_3) + \cdots + \log f(x_n) \tag{2}$$

and taking the derivative of this equation with respect to M and equating to zero we have

$$\frac{1}{y} \cdot \frac{dy}{dM} = \frac{1}{f(x_1)} \cdot \frac{df(x_1)}{dM} + \frac{1}{f(x_2)} \cdot \frac{df(x_2)}{dM} + \text{etc.} \tag{3}$$

Now, there is a function $\phi(x)$ which when multiplied by $f(x)$ gives the derivative of $f(x)$. Therefore,

$$\frac{df(x)}{dx} = \phi(x) \cdot f(x) \tag{4a}$$

or

$$\phi(x) = \frac{df(x)}{f(x)}\,dx \tag{4b}$$

This can best be illustrated by an example. If we let

$$f(x) = 2x^3$$
$$df(x) = 6x^2\,dx$$

Since we said that

$$df(x) = \phi(x)f(x)\,dx$$

therefore, if

$$\phi(x) = 3/x$$

we would have

$$df(x) = 3/x \cdot 2x^3\,dx$$
$$= 6x^2\,dx$$

If we thus substitute equation (4b) into equation (3), we get

$$\phi(x_1)\frac{dx_1}{dM} + \phi(x_2)\frac{dx_2}{dM} + \cdots \text{ etc. } = 0$$

Now, if we say that the percentage error is the same no matter what the size of the measured quantity, we have

$$\frac{dx_1}{dM} = \frac{dx_2}{dM} = \frac{dx_3}{dM} = B$$

where B is a constant. Now, from before we had

$$x_1 + x_2 + x_3 + \cdots + x_n = 0 \tag{5}$$

and from the fact that

$$\frac{dx_1}{dM} = B$$

we then have

$$\phi(x_1) + \phi(x_2) + \phi(x_3) + \cdots + \phi(x_n) = 0 \tag{6}$$

It can be stated, from (5) and (6):

$$\phi(x_1) + \phi(x_2) + \phi(x_3) + \cdots + \phi(x_n) = Cx_1 + Cx_2 + Cx_3 + \text{ etc.} \tag{7}$$

If we now substitute into equation (7) the value of $\phi(x)$ given in equation (4b), we have

$$\frac{df(x_1)}{f(x_1)\,dx_1} + \frac{df(x_2)}{f(x_2)\,dx_2} + \cdots = Cx_1 + Cx_2 + \cdots \tag{8}$$

Since this must be true for any number of values, the corresponding values must be equal; therefore, we have

$$\frac{df(x)}{f(x)\,dx} = Cx \tag{9}$$

If we integrate this, we have

$$\log f(x) = \tfrac{1}{2}Cx^2 + D$$

where D is a constant as well as C; or by simplifying we have

$$f(x) = e^{\frac{1}{2}Cx^2 + D}$$

But now this is actually

$$f(x) = (e^{\frac{1}{2}Cx^2})(e^{D})$$

But e^D is also a constant. Let us call this constant K and we have

$$f(x) = Ke^{\frac{1}{2}Cx^2} = y \tag{10}$$

If we examine equation (10) we realize that C must be negative since the probability must be decreasing as the value of x increases. That is, large errors are improbable. Let us let $C = -2h^2$ so that h and x are consistent. Then we have

$$y = Ke^{-h^2x^2} \tag{11}$$

It remains to evaluate the constant K. Since we desire the scale of our curve to be such that the ordinate y at any point will represent the probability of the size of an error given by x_1 and since we have stated that the sum of the probabilities of all possible errors must equal one, we then must have

$$\int_{-\infty}^{+\infty} Ke^{-h^2x^2} \cdot dx = 1$$

Since the curve is symmetrical about $x = 0$, we then know that

$$\int_{0}^{+\infty} Ke^{-h^2x^2} \cdot dx = \frac{1}{2}$$

If we let $t = hx$
$$dt = h\,dx$$
and $dx = dt/h$

we have

$$\frac{1}{2} = \frac{K}{h} \int_{0}^{\infty} e^{-t^2} \cdot dt$$

It could be shown that the above integral

$$\int_{0}^{\infty} e^{-t^2} \cdot dt = \frac{\sqrt{\pi}}{2}$$

though it is beyond the scope of this text. Hence,

$$\frac{1}{2} = \frac{K}{h}\frac{\sqrt{\pi}}{2}$$

or

$$K = \frac{h}{\sqrt{\pi}}$$

If we substitute this back into equation 11, we get

$$y = \frac{h}{\sqrt{\pi}} e^{-h^2 x^2} \tag{12}$$

Recalling that we neglected the differential dx at the time, we can now say that

$$p = y \, dx = \frac{h}{\sqrt{\pi}} e^{-h^2 x^2} \cdot dx \tag{13}$$

This is the equation of the normal probability density curve (one-dimensional).

appendix C / writing a taping specification

C–1 Taping Specifications

If we desire to design a procedure that will afford a precision of
1:10,000 when measuring with a steel tape, a good understanding of
the equipment and its use, as well as of the systematic errors involved,
will be necessary.

STEP 1. Let us assume (all errors being maximum) that:

(a) A good 100-ft steel tape (weight 0.0084 lb/ft) is available and
can be compared with a standard to ±0.004 ft.

(b) A taping thermometer is available, reliable to ±1°F; and the
air temperature recorded is not more than about ±3°F
different from the tape temperature.

(c) The tape will be used with both ends supported, held horizon-
tally, with a tension of 14 lb; and compared with the standard
using this method of support at this tension.

(d) A tensiometer (spring balance) is available, reliable to ±1 lb.

(e) The end-marking of tapelengths is done by suspending plumb
bobs with an expertness that gives a maximum error of
±0.007 ft.

(f) The tape ends are at the same elevation to within 0.5 ft.

(g) The tape has a cross section of 0.25 in. × 0.010 in.

STEP 2. Analysis (see tabulation of this analysis):

(a) *Tape Comparison.* It is expected that any systematic error
(difference in length between working tape and standard tape)
is cared for by a correction, and whatever error remains E_l is
less than 0.004 ft. While its sign is unknown, it does nonethe-
less accumulate directly.

(b) *Temperature.* There may be either a plus or a minus error of $\pm 3°F$ in reported temperature at each tape-length. This will be compensatory, not cumulative ($K = 0.00000645$ for steel).

$$E_t = KL(\Delta t)$$

Note: Some persons may validly argue that while we may miss the correct temperature value by being either too high or too low, thus making an error, the correct temperature will in reality be either consistently lower or consistently higher by reason of the consistency of the layers of air near the ground. Since this is true, they argue, the tape will have a consistent error in length, thus cumulative and not compensatory. Obviously, on the basis of this assumption the E_t should be regarded as cumulative—just as is the preceding E_l.

(c) *Pull.* The tensiometer may give an erroneous reading (or be read erroneously) by ± 1 lb for each tape-length, and the sign is not known. This is compensatory, not cumulative ($E = 30 \times 10^6$ psi for steel).

$$E_p = \frac{PL}{AE}$$

The pull error in the table is a simple computation for a pull variation of 1 lb in the formula.

(d) *Sag.* The major (cumulative) sag error is already compensated in the tape comparison [paragraph (a) above]. If an error of ± 1 lb of tension is still possible, the sag will be plus or minus some computed value. This is compensatory, not cumulative.

$$E_s = \frac{W^2L}{24P^2}$$

The sag correction must be computed for $P = 13$ lb and then for $P = 15$ lb. Half the difference of these two values gives an average sag error for ± 1 lb of P in that range.

(e) *Slope (gradient).* If one end of the tape is 0.5 ft higher or lower than the other when read, there will be the possibility of a distance error ranging from 0.000 to 0.125, always effectively shortening the tape. This will be cumulative, not compensatory (since its value is always on the same side of zero).

$$E_g = \frac{(\Delta h)^2}{2L}$$

SUMMARY AND COMPUTATION OF RANDOM TAPING ERRORS
(Computed for 10,000 ft or 100 tape-lengths)

Step 3 Error (E)	Value of error per tape-length	Nature	Error for 10,000 ft (E)	E^2
Length E_L	± 0.004	Cumul.	$\pm 0.004(100)$ $= \pm 0.4$	0.160
Temp. E_t	$\pm 0.00000645(100)(3) = \pm 0.0019$	Comp. (?)	$\pm 0.0019\sqrt{100}$ $= \pm 0.019$	0.00036
Pull E_p	$\pm \dfrac{(1)(100)}{(0.25 \times 0.010)(30 \times 10^6)} = \pm 0.0013$	Comp.	$\pm 0.0013\sqrt{100}$ $= 0.013$	0.000169
Sag E_s	$\pm \dfrac{1}{2}\left[\dfrac{(0.0084 \times 100)^2(100)}{24(13)^2} - \dfrac{(0.0084 \times 100)^2(100)}{24(15)^2}\right]$ $= \pm \dfrac{1}{2}[0.0174 - 0.0131] = \dfrac{0.0043}{2} = \pm 0.0022$	Comp.	$\pm 0.0022\sqrt{100}$ $= \pm 0.022$	0.00048
Slope E_g	$\pm \dfrac{(0.5)^2}{2(100)} = +0.00125$ (Cannot be minus in this context. Why?)	Cumul.	$+0.00125(100)$ $= +0.125$	0.0156
Marking E_m	± 0.007	Comp.	$\pm 0.007\sqrt{100}$ $= \pm 0.070$	0.0049
Σ				0.1816

$$\text{Total } E = \pm\sqrt{\sum E^2} = \pm\sqrt{0.1816} = \pm 0.425$$

$$\text{Precision} = \pm\frac{0.425}{10,000} = \pm\frac{1}{23,000}$$

(*f*) *Marking*. The ±0.007-ft error is compensatory, not cumulative.

STEP 3. Compute the above estimated good procedure (say, for 10,000 ft) and seek to ascertain the precision of the method.

STEP 4. It becomes immediately apparent that this procedure is too meticulous for 1:10,000 precision, and certain specifications can be relaxed. The largest contributor of error is E_L: note that if the tape comparison were made to ±0.002 ft, the final E (all else being unchanged) would be ±0.248 and the precision would show up as 1:40,000 for the procedure. However, for the present case, the procedure is uneconomically stringent for the precision desired, and the specifications may be amended, say, as follows:

(*a*) In tape comparison, find length to ±0.006 ft;
(*b*) In tension, allow ±2 lb;
(*c*) In temperature, expect to know within ±5°F;
(*d*) In end-marking, permit ±0.01 ft.

Step 4

Error (E)	Value of error per tape-length	Nature	Error for 10,000 ft (E)	E^2
E_L	±0.006	Cumul.	±0.600	0.360
E_t	±0.0032	Comp.	±0.032	0.0010
E_p	±0.0026	Comp.	±0.026	0.0007
E_s	±0.0028	Comp.	±0.028	0.0008
E_g	±0.00125	Cumul.	±0.125	0.0156
E_m	±0.01	Comp.	±0.10	0.010
Σ				0.3881

$$\text{Total } E = \pm\sqrt{\textstyle\sum E^2} = \pm\sqrt{0.3881} = \pm0.624$$

$$\text{Precision} = \frac{0.624}{10,000} = \frac{1}{16,000}$$

This is seen to be approaching the desired precision. Once a proper-sized error is anticipated per 10,000 ft (i.e., ± 1 ft), then the specifications for the procedure should be carefully written.

appendix D | classifications and standards
of accuracy (U.S. Coast
and Geodetic Survey)

TABLE 1   TRIANGULATION

	First-order			Second-order		Third-order
	Class I (Special)	Class II (Optimum)	Class III (Standard)	Class I	Class II	
Principal uses	Urban surveys, scientific studies	Basic network	All other	Area networks and supplemental cross arcs in national net	Coastal areas, inland waterways and engineering surveys	Topographic mapping
*Spacings of arcs or principal stations**	Stations: 1–5 miles or greater as required	Arcs: 60 miles Stations: 10–15 miles	Stations: 10–15 miles	Stations: 4–10 miles	As required	As required
Strength of figure						
$\sum R_1$ between bases						
Desirable limit	25	60	80	80	100	125
Maximum limit	30	80	110	120	130	175
Single figure Desirable limit						
R_1	5	10	15	15	25	25
R_2	10	30	50	70	80	120
Maximum limit						
R_1	10	25	25	25	40	50
R_2	15	60	80	100	120	170

TABLE 2 TRAVERSE

	First-order	Second-order	Third-order
Number of azimuth courses between azimuth checks not to exceed	15	25	50
Astronomical azimuth: Probable error of result	0.5"	2.0"	5.0"
Azimuth closure at azimuth check points not to exceed*	2 sec $\sqrt{N}$ or 1.0 sec per station	10 sec $\sqrt{N}$ or 3.0 sec per station	30 sec $\sqrt{N}$ or 8.0 sec per station
Distance measurements accurate within	1 in 35,000	1 in 15,000	1 in 7,500
After azimuth adjustment, closing error in position not to exceed*	0.66 ft $\sqrt{M}$ or 1 in 25,000	1.67 ft $\sqrt{M}$ or 1 in 10,000	3.34 ft $\sqrt{M}$ or 1 in 5,000

N is the number of stations for carrying azimuth.

M is the distance in miles.

* The expressions for closing errors in traverse surveys are given in two forms. The expression containing the square root is designed for longer lines where higher proportional accuracy is required. The formula which gives the smaller permissible closure should be used.

Base measurement						
Actual error not to exceed	1 part in 300,000	1 part in 300,000	1 part in 300,000	1 part in 300,000	1 part in 150,000	1 part in 75,000
Probable error not to exceed	1 part in 1,000,000	1 part in 1,000,000	1 part in 1,000,000	1 part in 1,000,000	1 part in 500,000	1 part in 250,000
Triangle closure						
Average not to exceed	1″	1″	1″	1.5″	3″	5″
Maximum seldom to exceed	3″	3″	3″	5″	5″	10″
Side checks						
Ratio of maximum difference of logs of sides to tab. diff. for 1″ of log sine of smallest angle	1.5	1.5–2	2	2–4	4	10–12
Or in side equation test, average corr. to direction not to exceed	0.3″	0.4″	0.4″	0.6″	0.8″	2″
Astro. Azimuths						
Spacing-figures	6–8	6–10	8–10	8–10	10–12	r2–15
Probable error	0.3″	0.3″	0.3″	0.3″	0.5″	2.0″
Closure in length (also position when applicable) after side and angle conditions	1 part in 100,000	1 part in 50,000	1 part in 25,000	1 part in 20,000	1 part in 10,000	1 part in 5,000

TABLE 3 LEVELING

	First-order	Second-order		Third-order
		Class I	Class II	
Spacing of lines and cross-lines	60 miles	25–35 miles	6 miles	Not specified
Average spacing of permanently marked bench marks along lines, not to exceed	1 mile	1 mile	1 mile	3 miles
Length of sections	$\frac{1}{2}$–1 mile	$\frac{1}{2}$–1 mile	$\frac{1}{2}$–1 mile	Not specified
Check between forward and backward running between fixed elevations or loop closures, not to exceed	4 mm $\sqrt{K}$ or 0.017 ft $\sqrt{M}$	8.4 mm $\sqrt{K}$ or 0.035 ft $\sqrt{M}$	8.4 mm $\sqrt{K}$ or 0.035 ft $\sqrt{M}$	12 mm $\sqrt{K}$ or 0.05 ft $\sqrt{M}$

K is the distance in kilometers.
M is the distance in miles.

appendix E / the geoid

It is thought desirable to introduce here some basic concepts of the shape of the earth on which we live because of our increasing knowledge thereof and the increasing need to know more about it. Though we have inhabited the earth for thousands of years, we still have not ascertained all we need to know about its shape and size. The following discussion is adapted in large part from *Special Publication No. 229* (1941) by J. A. Duerksen, U.S. Coast and Geodetic Survey.

A self-attracting fluid mass sufficiently far away from other attracting masses will assume the shape of a spheroid of revolution if it rotates through its center of gravity. If its density is uniform throughout, the spheroid will be an exact ellipsoid. In the case of the earth, our best evidence indicates that it is essentially a fluid mass beneath its crust, that it has a specific gravity of about 10 at the center and about $2\frac{1}{2}$ at the surface, and that it rotates about its center of gravity. Most of our rocks at the surface, for instance, have a specific gravity of $2\frac{1}{2}$ or so; solar observation furnishes information on its fairly stable rotation; and nothing to date discounts the fluid mass theory of its composition.

Therefore, when the earth is treated as a rotating fluid mass with its estimated variation of specific gravity and with the proper rotational speed, it has been calculated that the surface of the spheroid of revolution will almost exactly match that of an ellipsoid having its major and minor axes equal to the spheroid. The greatest variation between the two will occur at about latitude 45°, where the two surfaces will be about 3 meters apart.

The outermost surface of such a theoretical spheroid of revolution is an equipotential surface and is everywhere perpendicular to the direction of gravity. The outermost surface of the earth's oceans is obviously an equipotential surface and perpendicular to the direction of gravity, so we call this surface the *geoid*. The continuation of this equipotential surface under the continents forms the remainder of the geoid. Other equipotential surfaces above the ocean's surface could have been chosen as the geoid, but the geoid of mean sea level has been universally adopted. The ellipsoid most nearly coinciding with the geoid has been chosen as the surface of reference for geoidal measurements in the "horizontal" directions, i.e., in planes normal to gravity.

Ideally, all distances and angles measured on the earth should be reduced directly to the ellipsoid. Unfortunately, however, we do not know the relation between the geoid (actual) and the ellipsoid (theoretical). A basic difficulty is that the geoid is not nearly as smooth as the ellipsoid: it has undulations arising from local variations in density and concentration of masses (e.g., mountains) and voids (e.g., ocean "deeps"). The geoid is smooth enough, however, for most purposes to be fairly represented by a theoretical ellipsoid of revolution. An ellipsoid of revolution is, therefore, taken as the surface of reference in geodetic calculations, though there are three such spheroids in general use, as given in the accompanying table.

Spheroids	Equatorial radius (meters)	Polar semi-diameter (meters)	Flat-tening*
Bessel (1841): European	6,377,397	6,356,079	1/299.2
Clarke (1866): North American	6,378,206	6,356,584	1/295.0
International, after Hayford (1909): Adopted in 1924	6,378,388	6,356,912	1/297.0

* Flattening: Difference between Eq.R. and P.S-D. divided by P.S-D.

Latitude and longitude based on one of these spheroids could differ considerably from latitude and longitude based on another.

Further studies are constantly in progress to obtain a better ellipsoid. For instance, in 1956 the Army Map Service (U.S.) completed the two longest arcs ever measured: from Capetown to Finland, and from Chile to Alaska. At stations along these arcs star observations were made to fix latitude and longitude of each point (astronomic position), to be compared with the latitude and longitude computed by distance measurements along the arcs (geodetic position). Many other similar observations have been made by geodesists of many nations.

The *geodetic* position of a triangulation or traverse station is referred to a point on the celestial sphere (the sphere of "infinite" radius centered at our earth's "center") defined by the normal to the *ellipsoid* of reference. The *astronomic* position is referred to the point on the celestial sphere defined by the plumb line at the station, i.e., the line normal to the *geoid* at the station. If there is an angle between these two lines (between the normal to the ellipsoid and the plumb line) at any station, this is called the "deflection of the vertical" at that station.

The deflection of the vertical has two components, one in the meridian (N–S) and the other in the prime vertical (E–W). The difference between geodetic and astronomical latitudes of a station is the deflection in the meridian; the difference between the geodetic and astronomical longitudes multiplied by the cosine of the latitude is the deflection in the prime vertical.

Deflections of the vertical can be discovered for stations on continental land masses, where opportunity exists for connecting widely separated observation stations. This permits observers to discover and measure local undulations of the geoid. Knowing these deflections permits corrections to the astronomically determined latitudes and longitudes, sometimes of considerable magnitude.

EXAMPLE. Certain deflections of the vertical found to exist in the U.S. are given here, with position error in miles:

Columbus, Ga.	09.3″	0.2⁻ mile (approx.)
Point Arena, Calif.	18.9″	0.3⁺ mile (approx.)
Salt Lake City	17.5″	0.3⁻ mile (approx.)
Forest Park, L. I.	07.2″	0.1⁺ mile (approx.)

These vertical deflections, once ascertained, are no longer a problem. But if they cannot be determined, as on an isolated island, the position of the island as fixed by astronomic observation can be greatly in error. This is particularly true if a severe local gravity anomaly should exist, such as an extensive deep in the sea to one side of a huge land mass on the island itself. Certain islands recently connected to continents by new electronic distance-measuring methods (e.g., Shoran, Hiran, etc.) have been thus found to be star-positioned as much as 5 or 6 miles in error.

Measurements are today being made of deflections of the vertical and of the value of gravity in an effort to determine an ellipsoid that will more closely fit the geoid, as also to discover gravity anomalies that result in positioning errors. Gravimetric measuring devices, star-rockets, solar eclipses, and artificial satellites are being or will be used to complete the study. We still have much to learn, but much more information about the size and shape of the earth can be expected in the next few decades, because it is becoming increasingly important that we have such information.

Practically, pin-point navigation of supersonic aircraft, of missiles, and of underseas craft cannot be expected to be without its difficulties, for the inertial guidance systems used therefor already surpass in accuracy our knowledge of positions on the earth. The launching of vehicles into space depends on our knowledge of gravity, latitude, longitude, and deflection of the vertical at and near the launching sites. This is apparent if we consider the magnification of a slight aiming error induced by a local geoidal undulation when launching a rocket to the moon or to one of the planets.

Geodetic satellites now being placed into orbit around the earth promise much information for a better geodetic picture of the earth's shape in the very near future. Sightings on these passing bodies (optical and/or radio) will enable us to pin-point earth positions with much greater accuracy than ever possible heretofore.

appendix F | *the probability distribution curve*

While the normal *probability density* curve has been adduced as a pattern of normalcy for data such as measurements of a quantity, this (bell-shaped) curve is both difficult to draw and difficult to analyze. In practice, therefore, it is not frequently used. Instead, the normal probability distribution curve is employed.

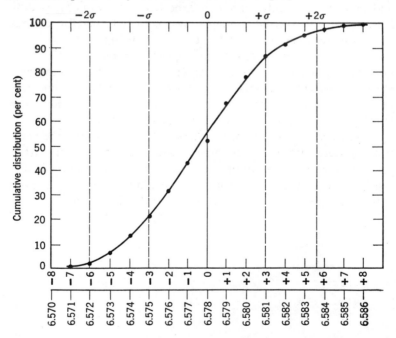

FIGURE F1 Cumulative frequency (normal probability) distribution curve.

The normal *probability distribution* curve is essentially a plot of the cumulative number of values (or errors) against the same abscissa as before, the value of the quantity (or error). Using the cumulative technique for the example of Art. 4–4 (the one with 439 observations) we have:

Value (feet) x	No. of occurrences f	Residual (or variation) v (1,000ths)	Cumul. no. of occurrences	% of No. of occurrences	Adjusted* % of occurrences
6.571	1	−7	1	0.2	0.2
6.572	8	−6	9	2.0	2.0
6.573	18	−5	27	6.2	6.1
6.574	27	−4	54	12.3	12.3
6.575	36	−3	90	20.5	20.4
6.576	43	−2	133	30.3	30.2
6.577	53	−1	186	42.4	42.3
6.578	55	0	241	54.9	54.8
6.579	53	+1	294	67.0	66.8
6.580	46	+2	340	77.4	77.3
6.581	36	+3	376	85.6	85.4
6.582	26	+4	402	91.6	91.4
6.583	15	+5	417	95.0	94.8
6.584	13	+6	430	97.9	97.7
6.585	7	+7	437	99.5	99.3
6.586	2	+8	439	100.0	99.8
6.5782 (mean)	439 n			* Explained subsequently	

The plot of this curve on the same abscissa as Fig. 6 (Art. 4–6) will give the curve shown in Fig. F1.

This is the cumulative frequency curve or the frequency distribution curve, drawn in as a smooth "S" curve to fit the points. Superimposed thereon are the values of $\pm \sigma_s$, which normally will fall on the straight portion of the S-curve. The $\pm 2\sigma_s$ positions, and the $\pm 3\sigma_s$ positions do not. These might be checked, incidentally, against the percentages of Arts. 5–9 and 5–12 to see if they contain the correct percentages of occurrences (cf. table of Art. 5–13). They would, of course, check properly in a theoretically correct distribution of an infinite number of random variables, and check fairly well in any good distribution of errors (or values).

The Probability Distribution Curve | 117

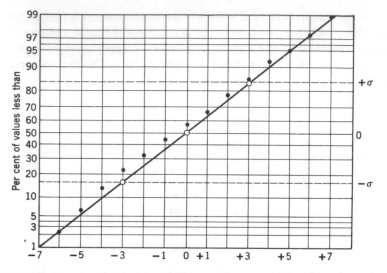

FIGURE F2   Set of 439 observations on a distant rod (plotted on arithmetic probability paper).

Still simpler methods of representing a frequency distribution have been developed, one of which is shown in Fig. F2.   The plotting is accomplished on the same abscissa as before, but the ordinate (%) scale has been expanded at both top and bottom to straighten out the loops of the "S" in the preceding distribution curve.   This plot is done on what is termed "arithmetic probability paper," available in several slightly different forms.

The result of plotting a truly normal distribution of errors (or of values) on this "arithmetic" paper is a straight line.   In fact, the straight line representing the data is drawn from only two (or three) known values: (1) The mean value; (2) $+\sigma_s$ value (and the $-\sigma_s$ value as a check).   This straight line is known as the line of "best fit," and is theoretically the truly best representation of all the values.

Before plotting the values, however, since we are using a finite segment of an infinite series, statisticians insist that we can never plot 100%.   By virtue of similar reasoning as in Arts. 4–2 and 4–3, we use an "adjusted percentage" for the plotting position of each error (or value).   This is found simply by the formula:

$$\frac{\text{Cumul. number of occurrences}}{(n + 1)} = \text{Adjusted percentage}$$

For example (in the preceding columnar form), these are the first few values:

$$1/440 = 0.2\%$$
$$9/440 = 2.0\%$$
$$27/440 = 6.1\%$$
$$\text{etc.}$$

Examination of the curve of Fig. F2 against the actual plotted points shows a very good correlation or "fit" of the points. This indicates that the set of measured values (the 439 observations on a distant rod) are normally distributed about the mean value, 6.578 ft. This, in turn, means that there is a 68.3% certainty that the true or correct value lies between 6.575 and 6.581, the $+\sigma$ and $-\sigma$ positions on the plot.

It is, in fact, this version of the normal distribution curve that is accepted almost universally as a test of the normalcy of the data gathered in measurements. By plotting the "best fit" line, using the mean and the sigma, and then plotting the actual values of the data, we obtain a good visualization of the distribution of values, of scatter, and of precision.

A further example is given here, this one using results of daily tests made on the effluent from an industrial waste treatment plant during the month of April, 1961. At issue here is the efficacy of the removal process.

EXAMPLE. The percentage of BOD (Biological Oxygen Demand) for each day of the month was found at one of West Virginia Pulp and Paper Company's industrial waste-treatment plants. From the data given (percentage of removal), determine the mean for the month, the standard deviation, etc., and plot the data on arithmetic probability paper.

April	1	80.7%	April	6	80.2%	April	11	81.6%
	2	87.6%		7	72.6%		12	79.3%
	3	87.0%		8	78.4%		13	79.3%
	4	82.6%		9	72.1%		14	80.1%
	5	83.0%		10	79.6%		15	72.6%
April	16	74.8%	April	21	78.4%	April	26	71.4%
	17	73.6%		22	80.4%		27	73.3%
	18	78.8%		23	78.2%		28	75.9%
	19	75.3%		24	81.5%		29	79.8%
	20	77.7%		25	79.1%		30	79.9%

Note: Here is the frequency distribution table. Because very few values occur more than once, this table differs slightly from that of Art. 4–4, where there were many values repeated.

Value (X)	Cumul. no.	Variation (v)	fv^2	Adjusted % of occurrence
71.4	1	−7.2	51.84	3.2
72.3	2	−6.3	39.69	6.5
72.6	3	−6.0	36.00	9.8
73.3	4	−5.3	28.09	12.9
73.6	5	−5.0	25.00	16.1
74.8	6	−3.8	14.44	19.4
75.3	7	−3.3	10.89	22.6
75.9	8	−2.7	7.29	25.8
76.2	9	−2.4	5.76	29.0
77.7	10	−0.9	0.81	32.3
78.2	11	−0.4	0.16	35.5
78.4	12	−0.2	0.04	38.7
78.4	13	−0.2	0.04	41.9
78.8	14	+0.2	0.04	45.2
79.1	15	+0.5	0.25	48.4
79.3	16	+0.7	0.49	51.6
79.3	17	+0.7	0.49	54.8
79.6	18	+1.0	1.00	58.1
79.8	19	+1.2	1.44	61.3
79.9	20	+1.3	1.69	64.6
80.1	21	+1.5	2.25	67.8
80.2	22	+1.6	2.56	71.0
80.4	23	+1.8	3.24	74.2
80.7	24	+2.1	4.41	77.4
81.5	25	+2.9	8.41	80.6
81.6	26	+3.0	9.00	83.9
82.6	27	+4.0	16.00	87.0
83.0	28	+4.4	19.36	90.3
87.0	29	+8.4	70.56	93.5
87.6	30	+9.0	81.00	96.9

$\sum = 2{,}358.4$ $\qquad\qquad \sum v^2 = 442.24$

$$\text{Mean} = \frac{2{,}358.4}{30} = 78.6$$

$$\sigma_s = \sqrt{\sum v^2/(n-1)} = \sqrt{442.24/29} = \sqrt{15.25} = \pm 3.91$$

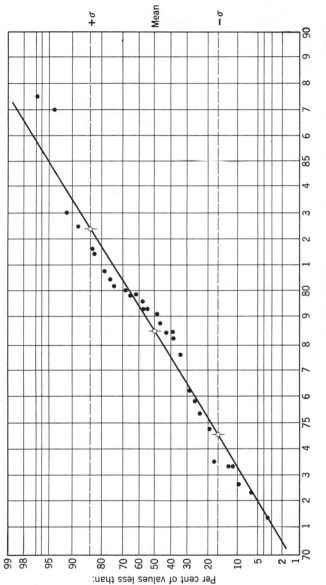

FIGURE F3 Efficiency of BOD removal at industrial waste-treatment plant during the month of April 1961 (arithmetic probability plot).

The curve is now plotted on arithmetic probability paper simply by plotting the mean (78.6) and the $+\sigma$ value ($78.6 + 3.9 = 82.5$); the $-\sigma$ value is also plotted as a check ($78.6 - 3.9 = 74.7$).

By also plotting the individual values, it will become apparent that the data of this problem are distributed in a fairly normal pattern. Were this not so, it would be evident after a little experience with such plotting.

FREQUENCY DISTRIBUTION TABULATION SHEET

Values (X)	Tally Space	f	X	v	fv	fv^2
Total [Σ]						

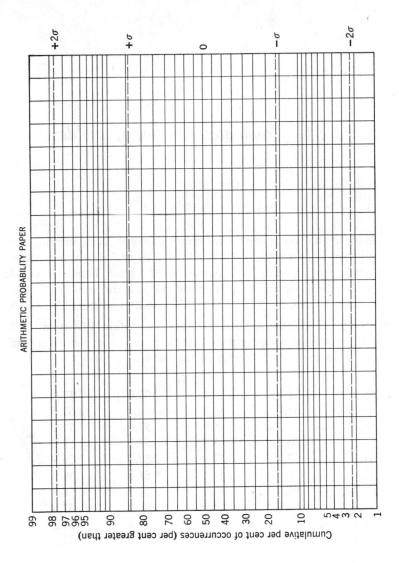

ARITHMETIC PROBABILITY PAPER

Cumulative per cent of occurrences (per cent greater than)

99 98 97 96 95 90 80 70 60 50 40 30 20 10 5 4 3 2 1

+2σ   +σ   0   −σ   −2σ

appendix G / computer solution of problems

Since digital computers have come into our lives, offering new facility for solution of problems and handling of data, some examples of their programming and operation are given here. A simple standard deviation problem is solved on four different computers: the Clary DE-60, the LGP-30, the IBM 1620, and the CDC 160-A.

EXAMPLE. The following are three groups of data, fifty items each. Find the standard deviation for each group, the mean for each group, and the standard error of the mean.

GROUP 1

56.9	57.1	54.4	58.0	57.1
58.1	57.7	55.2	58.1	57.9
54.5	58.8	56.8	57.6	57.1
54.0	56.5	55.6	57.1	58.0
57.1	57.2	57.1	57.9	58.9
57.8	58.0	54.4	58.0	59.8
57.3	58.3	54.9	57.3	58.2
57.9	58.5	54.5	56.9	57.9
58.1	58.1	54.3	57.9	57.5
56.8	57.0	54.6	57.5	57.2

GROUP 2

51.8	54.5	53.5	52.1	51.9
49.1	54.2	52.1	51.3	52.6
51.9	54.8	53.6	51.1	52.4
51.1	54.8	55.7	53.9	51.3
51.5	52.0	54.5	51.0	52.4

52.8	53.0	54.6	51.0	53.0
49.9	53.3	54.9	52.1	52.7
51.3	52.0	54.3	53.8	53.2
53.0	53.2	53.9	53.5	52.0
52.5	54.8	53.3	51.5	51.6

GROUP 3

56.9	57.1	54.4	58.0	57.1
58.1	57.9	55.2	58.1	57.9
54.5	58.8	56.8	57.6	57.1
54.0	56.5	55.6	57.1	58.0
57.1	57.2	57.1	57.9	58.9
57.8	58.0	54.4	58.0	58.9
57.3	58.3	54.9	57.3	59.8
57.9	58.5	54.5	56.9	58.2
58.1	58.1	54.3	57.9	57.9
56.8	57.0	54.6	57.8	57.5

By the Clary DE-60:

Program for wired board:

Clary COMPUTER

Program STATISTICAL ANALYSIS Pg. 1
Programer S. SHADY MANHATTAN Colb Date 9/27/63 Of 3

NOTES	INST.	S	O	D	M	RESULT
INSTRUCTIONS:	1	K			Cp1 ≤1-1	
1. INSERT BOARD No. 12	2				SKIP	
2. INSERT Sq. RT. CARTRIDGE	3		T	01	≤1-1 P	
3. SET WLC @ 11	4	K		09		
4. SET Σ SWITCH @ P	5		T	D		
5. SET ASC TO No. OF	6	00	S÷			
DECIMALS DESIRED	7	Q		02/M	P	
6. CLEAR CHANNEL 1	8		⊞	05		
7. CLEAR CHANNEL 0	9	00	S	D		
8. SET TYPEWRITER TO	10	01	S÷		ASC 7	
PRINT 6 COLUMNS	11	01	T×		cp2	
OF 15 SPACES EACH	12		T	03	P	
9. PRESTORE 1 IN 00	13	Q		M		
10. IF WORKING WITH	14	05	T×			
RATES (mph, ft/sec,	15		T	04	C.R.	
etc.), PRESTORE 2	16				SKIP	
IN 07	17		T		>1-1 C.R.	
11. PRESS P1	18	01	T		P	
12. WHEN MACHINE STOPS,	19	02	T+		P	
ENTER "X" WITH A "+"	20	03	T	D	P	
OR "—" KEY TO PRESET	21		S÷		C.R.	
NUMBER OF	22	09	T	D	C.R.	
DECIMAL PLACES	23	07	T		cp2	
13. WHEN MACHINE STOPS,	24	Q			>2-3 P	
ENTER "f" WITH "+"	25	04	T			
KEY AS A WHOLE	26		÷		ASC 7	
NUMBER (frequency)	27	09	T		P	
14. REPEAT STEP 12 & 13	28	Q			≤2-3 P	
UNTIL ALL VALUES	29		T			

Clary COMPUTER

NOTES	INST.	S	O	D	M	RESULT
OF "X" & "f" HAVE BEEN	30	00	[S]		cP1	
ENTERED, THEN	31	K			cP2 ≤2-1	
ENTER "O" WITH "+"	32				SKIP	
KEY.	33	01	[S] —		≤2-1	
15. WHEN MACHINE STOPS	34		T	$^0/_M$	P	
AGAIN, ROLL CARRIAGE	35	K				
BACK TO TOP	36		T	D		
LINE.	37	00	[S] ÷			
IMPORTANT —	38	Q		03		
DO NOT RESET MARGIN	39		✕			
DO NOT MOVE CARRIAGE	40		T	$^0/_M$	P	
HORIZONTALLY.	41	09	[T] ✕			
16. WHEN MACHINE STOPS	42		T	05	P	
ENTER "X" AS BEFORE	43		T		SS CR	
WITH "+" OR "—" KEY	44		T		P	
(It is suggested that	45		T		P	
both the "X" & "f" values	46		T		P	
be read from the	47				>2-1 C2-2	
typewriter to avoid	48				S₂	
errors or omissions.)	49		T	06	P	
17. WHEN MACHINE STOPS,	50	03	[T]	D		
ENTER "f" AS BEFORE.	51				S₂	
AS A WHOLE NUMBER,	52	06	[T]	D		
WITH "+" KEY.	53		S ÷			
18. REPEAT STEPS 17 & 18	54	Q			P	
UNTIL ALL "X" & "f" VALUES	55	01	[T]		P	
HAVE BEEN RE-ENTERED	56	00	[T]		C.R.	
THEN ENTER "O" WITH	57	02	[T]		C.R.	
"+" KEY	58		[+]	00	C.R.	
	59	02	[T]		cP1	

NOTES	INST.	S	O	D	M	RESULT
19. PRINTS ARE:	60	02	[I]		P	
x_0 f_0 f_0x_0 v_0 f_0v_0 $f_0v_0^2$	61	04	[I]	D	P	
	62	05	[S]		P	
	63	03	[S]÷		C.R.	
x_n f_n f_nx_0 v_n f_nv_n $f_nv_n^2$	64		T		P	
Σf Σfx Σfv Σfv^2	65		T		P	
$\bar{x}$ M_H $\bar{v}$	66		T		P	
σ_s σ_m M_0	67	Q	+	01		
$\bar{x} = \frac{\Sigma fx}{\Sigma f} =$ ARITHMETIC MEAN	68		T	D	P	
$M_H =$ HARMONIC MEAN $= \frac{\Sigma f}{\Sigma 1/x}$	69		÷			
$\bar{v} =$ MEAN DEVIATION $= \frac{\Sigma fv}{\Sigma v}$	70	03	[S]+		C.R.	
$\sigma_s =$ STANDARD DIVIATION	71	00	[I]			
FROM MEAN $= \sqrt{\Sigma fv^2 / \Sigma(f-1)}$	72		⊞	02		
$\sigma_m =$ STANDARD ERROR	73	Q	−			
OF MEAN $= \sigma_s / \sqrt{\Sigma f}$	74	05	[I]	D		
$M_0 =$ PROBABLE TRUE VALUE	75		T			
$= \bar{x} + \bar{v}$	76		÷			
COMPARES:	77		T		P	

	CP	C	≤	>	INST.	S	O	D	M
	CP	C	≤	>	78		T		P
1-1	1	SS	1/3	17	79		T		P
1-2	30	P1 of P1-P2		P2 of P1-P2	80	Q		D	
1-3	59				81				SKIP
2-1	11	SS	31/33	47/PH					
2-2	23	47	SKIP	S1					
2-3	31	01	28	24					

Concerning Steps 24 & 28
Depending on the Contents of
07, Either M_A or M_H is in 01
Concerning Step 47

	INST.	S	O	D	M
≤ SKIP ; > SS; S1	89				SS/ADV

Solution. The answers are given here to the nearest tenth of a unit, though they could have been carried out further by using the same program at an ASC setting of 2, 3, etc.

Set No. 1

x	f	fx	v	fv	fv^2
54.0	1	54.0	3.1-	3.1-	9.6
54.3	1	54.3	2.8-	2.8-	7.8
54.4	2	108.8	2.7-	5.4-	14.6
54.5	2	109.0	2.6-	5.2-	13.5
54.6	1	54.6	2.5-	2.5-	6.3
54.9	1	54.9	2.2-	2.2-	4.8
55.2	1	55.2	1.9-	1.9-	3.6
55.6	1	55.6	1.5-	1.5-	2.3
56.5	1	56.5	.6-	.6-	.4
56.8	2	113.6	.3-	.6-	.2
56.9	2	113.8	.2-	.4-	.1
57.0	1	57.0	.1-	.1-	
57.1	6	342.6			
57.2	2	114.4	.1	.2	
57.3	2	114.6	.2	.4	.1
57.5	2	115.0	.4	.8	.3
57.6	1	57.6	.5	.5	.3
57.7	1	57.7	.6	.6	.4
57.8	1	57.8	.7	.7	.5
57.9	5	289.5	.8	4.0	3.2
58.0	4	232.0	.9	3.6	3.2
58.1	4	232.4	1.0	4.0	4.0
58.2	1	58.2	1.1	1.1	1.2
58.3	1	58.3	1.2	1.2	1.4
58.5	1	58.5	1.4	1.4	2.0
58.8	1	58.8	1.7	1.7	2.9
58.9	1	58.9	1.8	1.8	3.2
59.8	1	59.8	2.7	2.7	7.3

$\Sigma f = 50 \qquad 2853.4 = \Sigma fx \qquad \Sigma fv = 1.6- \qquad 93.2 = \Sigma fv^2$

$57.1 = \bar{x} \qquad M_h = 57.0 \qquad \sigma_s = 1.4 \qquad \sigma_m = .1 \qquad 57.1 = M_o$

Set No. 2

x	f	fx	v	fv	fv^2
49.1	1	49.1	3.6-	3.6-	13.0
49.9	1	49.9	2.8-	2.8-	7.8
51.0	2	102.0	1.7-	3.4-	5.8
51.1	2	102.2	1.6-	3.2-	5.1
51.3	3	153.9	1.4-	4.2-	5.9
51.5	2	103.0	1.2-	2.4-	2.9
51.6	1	51.6	1.1-	1.1-	1.2
51.8	1	51.8	.9-	.9-	.8
51.9	2	103.8	.8-	1.6-	1.3
52.0	3	156.0	.7-	2.1-	1.5
52.1	3	156.3	.6-	1.8-	1.1
52.4	2	104.8	.3-	.6-	.2
52.5	1	52.5	.2-	.2-	
52.6	1	52.6	.1-	.1-	
52.7	1	52.7			
52.8	1	52.8	.1	.1	
53.0	3	159.0	.3	.9	.3
53.2	2	106.4	.5	1.0	.5
53.3	2	106.6	.6	1.2	.7
53.5	2	107.0	.8	1.6	1.3
53.6	1	53.6	.9	.9	.8
53.8	1	53.8	1.1	1.1	1.2
53.9	2	107.8	1.2	2.4	2.9
54.2	1	54.2	1.5	1.5	2.3
54.3	1	54.3	1.6	1.6	2.6
54.5	2	109.0	1.8	3.6	6.5
54.6	1	54.6	1.9	1.9	3.6
54.8	3	164.4	2.1	6.3	13.2
54.9	1	54.9	2.2	2.2	4.8
55.7	1	55.7	3.0	3.0	9.0

$\Sigma f = 50 \qquad 2636.3 = \Sigma fx \qquad \Sigma fv = 1.3 \qquad 96.3 = \Sigma fv^2$

$52.7 = \bar{x} \qquad M_h = 52.6 \qquad \sigma_s = 1.4 \qquad \sigma_m = .1 \qquad 52.7 = M_o$

Set No. 3

x	f	fx	v	fv	fv^2
54.0	1	54.0	3.1-	3.1-	9.6
54.3	1	54.3	2.8-	2.8-	7.8
54.4	2	108.8	2.7-	5.4-	14.6
54.5	2	109.0	2.6-	5.2-	13.5
54.6	1	54.6	2.5-	2.5-	6.3
54.9	1	54.9	2.2-	2.2-	4.8
55.2	1	55.2	1.9-	1.9-	3.6
55.6	1	55.6	1.5-	1.5-	2.3
56.5	1	56.5	.6-	.6-	.4
56.8	2	113.6	.3-	.6-	.2
56.9	2	113.8	.2-	.4-	.1
57.0	1	57.0	.1-	.1-	
57.1	6	342.6			
57.2	1	57.2	.1	.1	
57.3	2	114.6	.2	.4	.1
57.5	1	57.5	.4	.4	.2
57.6	1	57.6	.5	.5	.3
57.8	2	115.6	.7	1.4	1.0
57.9	6	347.4	.8	4.8	3.8
58.0	4	232.0	.9	3.6	3.2
58.1	4	232.4	1.0	4.0	4.0
58.2	1	58.2	1.1	1.1	1.2
58.3	1	58.3	1.2	1.2	1.4
58.5	1	58.5	1.4	1.4	2.0
58.8	1	58.8	1.7	1.7	2.9
58.9	2	117.8	1.8	3.6	6.5
59.8	1	59.8	2.7	2.7	7.3

$$\Sigma f = 50 \qquad 2855.6 = \Sigma fx \qquad \Sigma fv = .6 \qquad 97.1 = \Sigma fv^2$$

$$= 57.1 = \bar{x} \qquad M_h = 57.0 \qquad \sigma_s = 1.4 \qquad \sigma_m = .1 \qquad 57.1 = M_o$$

By the LGP-30:

Program by Act Three Compiler:

```
Standard Deviation and Standard Error
February 6, 1964          Programmer: JJN'

sl'       dim'a'501''
          index'i''
          1';'i''
          0';'a';'n''
          cr'daprt'uc2's'lcl't'a'n'd'a'r'd' 'uc2'd'lcl'e'v'i'a't'i'o'n' '
          a'n'd' 'uc2's'lcl't'a'n'd'a'r'd' 'uc2'e'lcl'r'r'o'r'cr4'cr4''
s5'       read'a'i''
          rdxit'sl0''
          a'+'a'i';'a''
          n'i+'l';'n''
          i'i+'l';'i''
          use's5''
sl0'      0'flo'n';'nl''
          a'/'nl';'m''
          1';'i''
          0';'a''
sl5'      ['a'i'-'m']'x'['a'i'-'m']';'p''
          a'+'p';'a''
          for'i'step'l'until'n'rpeat'sl5''
          sqrt'['a'/'nl']';'sig''
          cr'cr'cr'daprt'n' 'uc2'='lcl' ''
          800'iprt'n''
          cr'daprt'uc2'm'lcl'e'a'n' 'uc2'='lcl' ''
          1608'print'm''
          cr'daprt'uc2's'lcl't'a'n'd'a'r'd' 'uc2'd'lcl'e'v'i'a't'i'o'n' 'uc2'='lcl' ''
          1608'print'sig''
          sig'/'['sqrt'['nl'-'.9999'99999'e'0']']';'sigm''
          cr'daprt'uc2's'lcl't'a'n'd'a'r'd' 'uc2'e'lcl'r'r'o'r' 'uc2'='lcl' ''
          1608'print'sigm''
          bkp8'use'sl''use'sl'''
```

Solution. All the surplus digits in the decimal region of the answers should, of course, be rounded off and discarded.

```
Data set 1

+569'+2'+581'+2'+545'+2'+540'+2'+571'+2'
+578'+2'+573'+2'+579'+2'+581'+2'+568'+2'
+571'+2'+577'+2'+588'+2'+565'+2'+572'+2'
+580'+2'+583'+2'+585'+2'+581'+2'+570'+2'
+544'+2'+552'+2'+568'+2'+556'+2'+571'+2'
+544'+2'+549'+2'+545'+2'+543'+2'+546'+2'
+580'+2'+581'+2'+576'+2'+571'+2'+579'+2'
+580'+2'+573'+2'+569'+2'+579'+2'+575'+2'
+571'+2'+579'+2'+571'+2'+580'+2'+589'+2'
+598'+2'+582'+2'+579'+2'+575'+2'+572'+2''

n =        50
Mean =     .57067788 e 02
Standard Deviation =    .13643199 e 01
Standard Error =    .19490278 e 00
```

Data set 2

```
+518'+2'+491'+2'+519'+2'+511'+2'+515'+2'
+528'+2'+499'+2'+513'+2'+530'+2'+525'+2'
+545'+2'+542'+2'+548'+2'+548'+2'+520'+2'
+530'+2'+533'+2'+520'+2'+532'+2'+548'+2'
+535'+2'+521'+2'+536'+2'+557'+2'+545'+2'
+546'+2'+549'+2'+543'+2'+539'+2'+533'+2'
+521'+2'+513'+2'+511'+2'+539'+2'+510'+2'
+510'+2'+521'+2'+538'+2'+535'+2'+515'+2'
+519'+2'+526'+2'+524'+2'+513'+2'+524'+2'
+530'+2'+527'+2'+532'+2'+520'+2'+516'+2''
```

n =   50
Mean =   .52725810 e 02
Standard Deviation =   .13867652 e 01
Standard Error =   .19810927 e 00

Data set 3

```
+569'+2'+581'+2'+545'+2'+540'+2'+571'+2'
+578'+2'+573'+2'+579'+2'+581'+2'+568'+2'
+571'+2'+579'+2'+588'+2'+565'+2'+572'+2'
+580'+2'+583'+2'+585'+2'+581'+2'+570'+2'
+544'+2'+552'+2'+568'+2'+556'+2'+571'+2'
+544'+2'+549'+2'+545'+2'+543'+2'+546'+2'
+580'+2'+581'+2'+576'+2'+571'+2'+579'+2'
+580'+2'+573'+2'+569'+2'+579'+2'+578'+2'
+571'+2'+579'+2'+571'+2'+580'+2'+589'+2'
+589'+2'+598'+2'+582'+2'+579'+2'+575'+2''
```

n =   50
Mean =   .57111776 e 02
Standard Deviation =   .13924974 e 01
Standard Error =   .19892818 e 00

By the IBM 1620:

Program by Fortran, and solution:

```
ENTER SOURCE PROGRAM, PUSH START
08300 C      IBM 1620 PROGRAM FOR STANDARD DEVIATION (FORTRAN WITH FORMAT)
08300 C      ARBITRARY LIMIT ON NUMBER OF SAMPLES (N) SET AT 100
08300        DIMENSION DATA(100)
08300      1 READ 40,N
08324        DO 2 I=1,N,5
08336      2 READ 50,DATA(I),DATA(I+1),DATA(I+2),DATA(I+3),DATA(I+4)
08564        SUM1=0.
08600        DO 7 I=1,N
08612      7 SUM1=SUM1+DATA(I)
08720        AN=N
08768        AMEAN=SUM1/AN
08816        SUM2=0.
08852        DO 13 I=1,N
08864        VAR=DATA(I)-AMEAN
08936     13 SUM2=SUM2+VAR*VAR
09032     16 DEVS=SQRT(SUM2/AN)
09092        DEVM=DEVS/SQRTF(AN-1.)
09164        PRINT 60,DEVS,DEVM,AMEAN
09212        GO TO 1
09220     40 FORMAT(I4)
09242     50 FORMAT(5F4.1)
09284     60 FORMAT(12HSIGMA SUB S F6.2,12HSIGMA SUB M F6.2,5HMEAN F6.2)
09396        END

PROG SW1 ON FOR SYMBOL TABLE, PUSH START
SW 1 OFF TO IGNORE SUBROUTINES, PUSH START

PROCESSING COMPLETE
16000 100000ORS
ENTER SUBROUTINES, PUSH START
1620 FORTRAN VER-2 SUBR SET 1    8/63
LOAD DATA
SIGMA SUB S    2.15SIGMA SUB M    .57MEAN    11.60
SIGMA SUB S    1.36SIGMA SUB M    .19MEAN    57.06
SIGMA SUB S    1.38SIGMA SUB M    .19MEAN    52.72
SIGMA SUB S    1.39SIGMA SUB M    .19MEAN    57.11
SIGMA SUB S    1.37SIGMA SUB M    .13MEAN    57.09
```

The 1st and 5th of the lines immediately above are results of other problems run at the same time; lines 2, 3, and 4 are the results of the example sets 1, 2, and 3 respectively.

By the CDC 160-A:

Program by Fortran, and solution:

```
C       MANHATTAN COLLEGE A K
        DIMENSION  A(150)
I       READ 1001,N
        READ 1000,(A(I),I=1,N)
        SUMA=0
        DO 2 I=1,N
2       SUMA=SUMA+A(I)
        SN=N
        SMEAN=SUMA/SN
        SUMB=0
        DO 3 I=1,N
        SVAR=A(I)-SMEAN
3       SUMB=SUMB+SVAR*SVAR
        SIGMAS=SQRTF(SUMB/SN)
        SIGMAM=SIGMAS/SQRTF(SN-1)
        PRINT 1002,SMEAN,SIGMAS,SIGMAM
        PAUSE 11
        GO TO 1
1000    FORMAT (10F8.2)
1001    FORMAT(I3)
 1002   FORMAT(6H MEAN=,F6.2,5X,11HSTAND DEV =,F6.2,5X,11HSTAND ERR =,
        1F6.2)
        END
MEAN= 57.06      STAND DEV =  1.36      STAND ERR =    .19
MEAN= 52.72      STAND DEV =  1.38      STAND ERR =    .19
MEAN= 57.11      STAND DEV =  1.39      STAND ERR =    .19
MEAN= 55.63      STAND DEV =  2.47      STAND ERR =    .20
```

index

Accidental error, 22
Accuracy, 1, 15, 22
  positional, 85
Adjustment, 63
Arithmetic mean, 8, 13, 22, 33
Arithmetic probability, 118, 122
Astronomic position, 114
Average, 8, 33, 56

Best value, 8, 13, 19, 20
Blunder, 9

Computers, 124
  CDC 160-A, 134
  Clary DE-60, 126
  IBM 1620, 133
  LGP-30, 131
Control system, 87
Correction, 11, 63
Correctness, 8

Deflection of vertical, 114
Deviation, 34 (*see also* Standard deviation)
Discrepancy, 9, 12
Distribution, 19

Ellipsoid of reference, 112, 114
Error, 1, 21
  accidental, 12, 16
  circular, 83

Error (*cont.*)
  conversion factors, 40
  cumulative, 9
  elliptical, 83
  instrumental, 10
  maximum, 39, 44, 50, 71
  natural, 10
  personal, 10
  practical application, 70
  probable, 37
  propagation, 49
  random, 12
  relative, 51
  sigma, 25
  standard (*see* Standard error)
  summary table, 39
  systematic, 9
  true, 8
  two-dimensional, 79
  and weights, 62
Estimation, 7

Fortran, 133, 134
Frequency, 33
Frequency distribution, 26, 117

Geodetic position, 114
Geodimeter, 75
Geoid, 112, 113
Gravity, 113, 115

Histogram, 18, 28, 93

Inch, 2, 4
Indexes, 58

Least square, 19

Mean, 13, 33
  arithmetic, 8, 13, 22, 33
  assumed, 30
  weighted, 56
Mean deviation, 34
Mean square error, 24, 25, 35
Measurement, 2, 5
  direct, 5
  indirect, 5
  rejection of, 43
  repeated, 42
Median, 33
Meter, 4
Mistake, 9
Mode, 33

National Bureau of Standards. 5
  inch, 2, 4

Precision, 1, 15, 22
Probability, 19, 93
Probability circle, 81
Probability curve, 18, 24, 28, 95
  density, 97, 101, 116
  distribution, 29, 116
  normal, 18, 29, 95
  skewed, 19
Probability ellipse, 80

Probable error, 37
Probable value, 20, 39

Range, 34
Readings, 7
Reliability, 33, 42, 56
Residual, 12, 21
Round-off, 92

Scatter, 34
Sigma error, 25, 35
Significance, 45
Significant figures, 90
Specifications, 73, 76, 102
Spheroid, 112, 113
Standard, 2, 4
Standard deviation, 24, 30, 35, 42,
  70, 124
Standard error, 25, 27, 45, 47, 62, 70,
  124
Standard error of difference, 45
Standard procedure, 72

Taping, errors, 102
  specifications, 102
True value, 13, 16, 21, 44

U. S. Coast and Geodetic Survey, 3,
  73, 107, 112

Variance, 19
Variation, 21, 25

Weights, 56, 59, 62, 65